Go for $^{197}_{79}\text{Au}$ in Chemistry with CGP!

It's not easy to score a top mark in Edexcel International GCSE Chemistry* — if you're after a Grade 8 or 9, you'll really have to know your onions. And your cations.

Fortunately, this CGP book is packed with extra-tough exam practice that'll test you on everything you'll need for the highest grades. There are hundreds of questions sorted by topic, plus two sections of mixed practice for a more realistic exam-style challenge.

But wait, there's more! There are fully-worked answers in the back of the book, so it's easy to check your answers and make sure you're on track for a great result.

* This book also covers all the hardest Chemistry topics from Edexcel's International GCSE Science Double Award.

CGP — still the best! ☺

Our sole aim here at CGP is to produce the highest quality books — carefully written, immaculately presented and dangerously close to being funny.

Then we work our socks off to get them out to you — at the cheapest possible prices.

Published by CGP

Editors:
Emma Clayton, Paul Jordin, Sam Mann

Contributors:
Chris Harris, Angela McGill, David Paterson, Louise Watkins

With thanks to Jamie Sinclair for the proofreading.

With thanks to Ana Pungartnik for the copyright research.

Data in the table on page 53 based on Figure SPM.4 from IPCC, 2013: Climate Change 2013: The Physical Science Basis. Working Group I Contribution to the Fifth Assessment Report of the Intergovernmental Panel on Climate Change.

ISBN: 978 1 78908 237 1

Clipart from Corel®
Illustrations by: Sandy Gardner Artist, email sandy@sandygardner.co.uk
Printed by Elanders Ltd, Newcastle upon Tyne.

Based on the classic CGP style created by Richard Parsons.

Contents

☑ Use the tick boxes to check off the topics you've completed.

Paper 2

The questions in this book test both Chemistry Paper 1 and Chemistry Paper 2 material. Some material is needed for Paper 2 only — we've marked Paper 2 questions in Sections 1-6 with brackets like this one.

If you're doing a Science (Double Award) qualification you don't need to learn the Paper 2 material.

Exam Tips

Exam Basics

1) For the Edexcel International GCSE in Chemistry,
   you'll sit two exam papers at the end of your course. ➡️

Paper	Time	No. of marks
1	2 hours	110
2	1 hr 15 mins	70

2) If you're doing the Edexcel International GCSE Science
   Double Award, you won't sit Paper 2.

3) Some material in the specification will only be tested in Paper 2.
   In Sections 1-6 of this book, the questions that cover Paper 2 material are marked with a Paper 2 bracket.

You Need to Understand the Command Words

Command words are the words in a question that tell you what to do.
If you don't know what they mean, you might not be able to answer the questions properly.

Describe This means you need to recall facts or write about what something is like.

Explain You have to give reasons for something or say why or how something happens.

Suggest You need to use your knowledge to work out the answer. It'll often be something you haven't been taught, but you should be able to use what you know to figure it out.

Calculate This means you'll have to use numbers from the question to work something out. You'll probably have to get your calculator out.

Here are a Few Handy Hints

1) **Always, always, always make sure you read the question properly.**
   This is a simple tip but it's really important. When you've got so much knowledge swimming round in your head it can be tempting to jump right in and start scribbling your answer down. But take time to make absolutely sure you're answering the question you've been asked.

2) **Take your time with unfamiliar contexts.**
   Examiners like to test you really understand what you've learnt by asking you to apply your knowledge in different ways. Some of these contexts can be quite tricky but don't let them trip you up — read all the information you're given really carefully and, if you don't understand it, read it again. You can make notes alongside the question or underline certain bits if it helps you to focus on the important information.

3) **Look at the number of marks a question is worth.**
   The number of marks gives you a pretty good clue as to how much to write. So if a question is worth four marks, make sure you write four decent points. And there's no point writing an essay for a question that's only worth one mark — it's just a waste of your time.

4) **Show each step in your calculations.**
   You might be a bit of a whizz at maths and be confident that your final answer to a question will be right, but everyone makes mistakes — especially when under the pressure of an exam. Always write things out in steps then, even if your final answer's wrong, you'll probably pick up some marks for your method.

5) **Pay attention to the time.**
   After all those hours of revision it would be a shame to miss out on marks because you didn't have time to even attempt some of the questions. If you find that you're really struggling with a question, just leave it and move on to the next one. You can always go back to it at the end if you've got enough time.

These handy hints might help you pick up as many marks as you can in the exams — but they're no use if you haven't learnt the stuff in the first place. So make sure you revise well and do as many practice questions as you can.

States of Matter

1 A scientist is investigating the properties of two gases:
bromine gas, Br_2, and nitrogen dioxide, NO_2.

a) The scientist makes a sample of bromine gas by heating liquid bromine until it evaporates.
Describe what happens to the particles when bromine evaporates.

....

....

....

....

....

[4]

The scientist sets up the apparatus shown on the right.
The table shows some information about the two gases,
bromine gas and nitrogen dioxide.

Gas	Colour	Molecular weight (g/mol)
Br_2	Brown	160
NO_2	Brown	46

b) The glass plates are removed at the same time.
Describe what the scientist will observe. Explain your answer.

....

....

....

....

....

[4]

c) The scientist repeats the experiment using only bromine gas.
This time she puts the bromine gas in a flask and attaches it
to an airless chamber, as shown on the right.

Suggest what the scientist will observe
when the tap is opened. Explain your answer.

....

....

....

....

[2]

[Total 10 marks]

2 This question is about solubility.

a) Which of the following is the correct definition of a saturated solution?

☐ **A** A solution where the maximum amount of solute has been dissolved.

☐ **B** A solution with equal amounts of solvent and solute.

☐ **C** A solution where the maximum amount of solvent has been dissolved.

☐ **D** A solution that contains more solvent than solute.

[1]

b) A student carries out an experiment to determine the water solubility of a compound at different temperatures. His results are shown in the table below.

Temperature (°C)	0	20	40	60	80	100
Solubility (g per 100 g of water)	11.5	16.0	25.0	37.5	54.0	76.0

i) Draw a graph to show this data. Include a curved line of best fit.

[4]

ii) The student plans to repeat his experiment using a temperature of 30 °C.
Use your graph to predict the mass of the compound that the student
will need to saturate 25 g of water at 30 °C.

mass .... g

[2]

[Total 7 marks]

Elements, Compounds and Mixtures

1   This question is about a metallic element, **X**.

The graph shows the mass and relative abundance of different isotopes of element **X**.

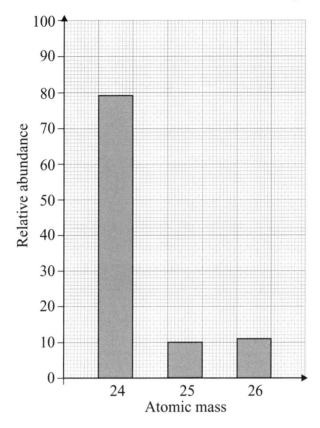

a)   i)   Calculate the relative atomic mass of **X**. Give your answer to one decimal place.

relative atomic mass = ...
[3]

ii)   Give the name of element **X**. Use the periodic table to help you.

....
[1]

b)   i)   Give the number of electrons in an atom of ^{25}**X**.

....
[1]

ii)   Explain why an atom of ^{25}**X** does not have an overall charge.

....

....
[1]

[Total 6 marks]

4

2   A scientist is separating some mixtures of substances.

a) The first mixture is of copper sulfate, silicon dioxide and water.
   Copper sulfate is a water-soluble substance.
   Silicon dioxide is a water-insoluble substance.

   Name two techniques that could be used to purify each of the copper sulfate and silicon dioxide.
   Explain why each technique is suitable.

   Technique 1: ....

   Explanation: ....

   ....

   Technique 2: ....

   Explanation: ....

   ....
                                                                                                              [4]

b) A second mixture consists of three liquids with boiling points of 50 °C, 65 °C and 80 °C.
   State a process that can be used to separate these substances.
   Explain how this process works, and why it is suitable.

   ....

   ....

   ....

   ....

   ....

   ....
                                                                                                              [4]

c) The third mixture contains a complex set of liquids that will react together if heated.
   Suggest a suitable technique that could be used to investigate the composition of the mixture.
   Explain your reasoning.

   Technique: ....

   Explanation: ....

   ....

   ....
                                                                                                              [2]

d) The fourth mixture is a solution of sodium chloride.
   The scientist wants to separate the water from the sodium chloride, then analyse the water.
   Explain why crystallisation is not a suitable method for the scientist to use.

   ....

   ....
                                                                                                              [1]
                                                                                                  [Total 11 marks]

Section 1 — Particles and Mixtures

3 A medicine comes in a 5.0 g sachet. It contains 120 mg of paracetamol per 5.0 g, along with various other ingredients.

a) Calculate the percentage of paracetamol in each sachet.

....%

[2]

The medicine contains several compounds called parabens. A sample of the medicine, along with pure samples of four parabens, was analysed by paper chromatography.

b) Explain how paper chromatography separates out the substances in the medicine. Do not include details of how you would carry out the practical in your answer.

....

....

....

....

....

[3]

c) The resulting chromatogram is shown below.

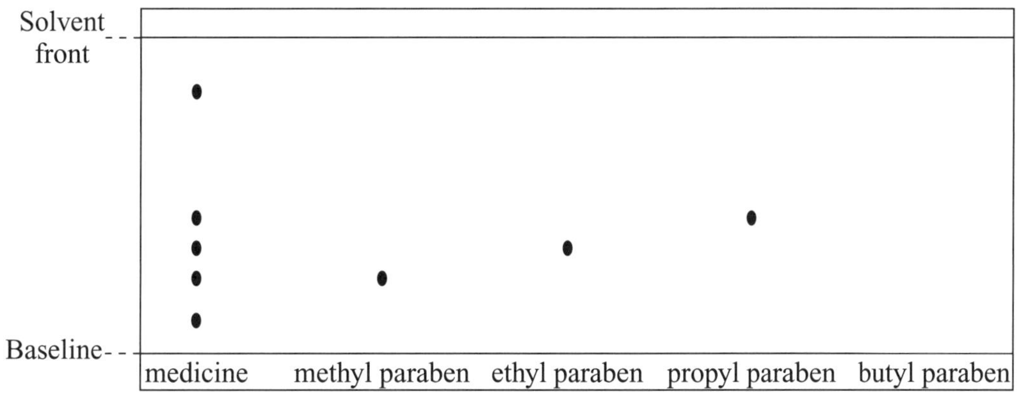

Calculate the R_f value for propyl paraben. Give your answer to an appropriate number of significant figures.

R_f = ...

[3]

d) The R_f value for butyl paraben, which is not found in the medicine, is 0.52.
Calculate the distance moved by butyl paraben on the chromatogram.
Mark its position on the chromatogram in part **c)**.

Distance = ... cm

[3]

A sample of ethanol is thought to be contaminated with ethyl paraben.
When separated from the ethanol, the contaminating substance was found
to have a melting point of 115-120 °C.

e) What does this information suggest about the purity of the contaminant? Explain your answer.

....

....

....

[2]

[Total 13 marks]

4 A substance, **Z**, is believed to be contaminated with an unknown impurity.

a) Describe how the impurity is likely to affect the boiling point of **Z**.

....

....

[1]

b) The impurity is believed to be one of substances **A**, **B** or **C**.
Describe how a paper chromatography experiment can be used to help
identify which, if any, of the impurities is present in substance **Z**.

....

....

....

[2]

c) Suggest how further paper chromatography experiments
could be used to give a more reliable result.

....

....

[2]

[Total 5 marks]

Exam Practice Tip

Think about the chemical properties of the substances within a mixture to decide how they might be
separated out. If a mixture described in an exam question contains several substances, then there's a
good chance you'll need to use more than one technique to separate them all.

Score:

35

The Periodic Table

1 This question is about the periodic table.

a) i) Which of the following elements forms an oxide that has a pH greater than 7 in solution?

☐ **A** lithium   ☐ **B** silicon   ☐ **C** boron   ☐ **D** hydrogen

[1]

ii) Explain your answer to part **a) i)** in terms of the position of the element in the periodic table.

....

....

[2]

b) Explain how aluminium's position in the periodic table is linked to its electronic configuration.

....

....

....

....

[3]

c) The diagram shows the trends in reactivity of non-metals and Group 1 and Group 2 metals. The arrows show trends of increasing reactivity.

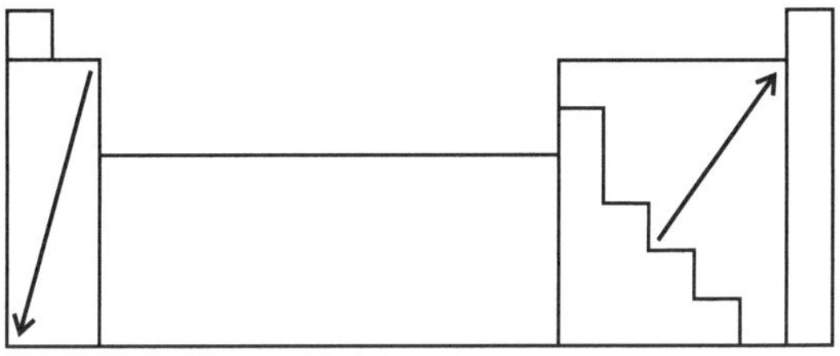

When metals and non-metals react, heat energy is given out. The amount of heat energy given out increases with the reactivity of the reactants. State which of the compounds below you would expect to give out the most heat energy when produced. Explain your reasoning.

Caesium chloride   Caesium iodide   Sodium chloride   Sodium iodide

....

....

....

....

[3]

[Total 9 marks]

Exam Practice Tip

A good knowledge of atomic structure and the periodic table will help you understand many aspects of chemistry — that's why the knowledge was developed after all. Don't forget you can refer to the periodic table in the exam and there's lots of information available there if you know how to read it.

Score: ☐

9

Types of Bonding

1 Metals and graphite have similarities and differences in their structure and their properties.

a) Give **two** similarities and **two** differences between graphite
and pure copper in terms of structure and bonding.

....

....

....

....

....

[4]

b) Explain why graphite is able to conduct electricity.

....

....

....

[2]

[Total 6 marks]

2 A student is investigating the electrical conductivity of calcium chloride
in various states. The diagram shows the circuit that he uses.

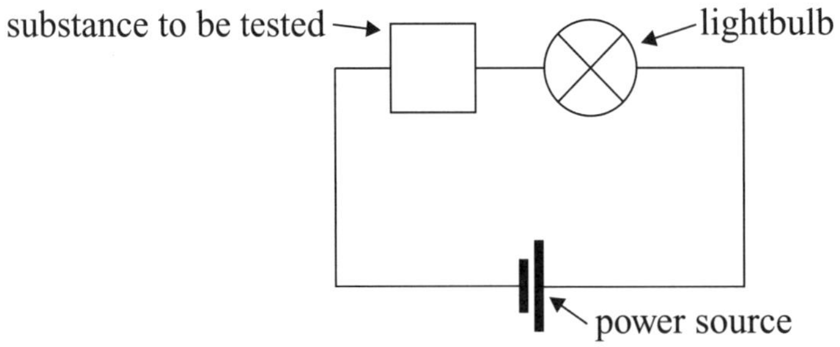

substance to be tested → ☐   ⊗ ← lightbulb

⊣⊢ ← power source

The student tests calcium chloride as both a solid and as an aqueous solution.
Predict the results of each experiment. Explain your answers.

Solid: ....

....

....

Aqueous: ....

....

....

[Total 4 marks]

Section 2 — The Periodic Table and Bonding

3   This question is about the bonding in hydrocarbons.

a) Ethene has the formula C_2H_4.
The diagram shows the outer shells of the atoms in ethene.

Label the diagram with the correct symbol for each atom, and turn it into a dot and cross diagram by showing the arrangement of the outer shell electrons.
Use dots to represent the electrons on the carbon atoms, and use crosses to represent the electrons on the hydrogen atoms.

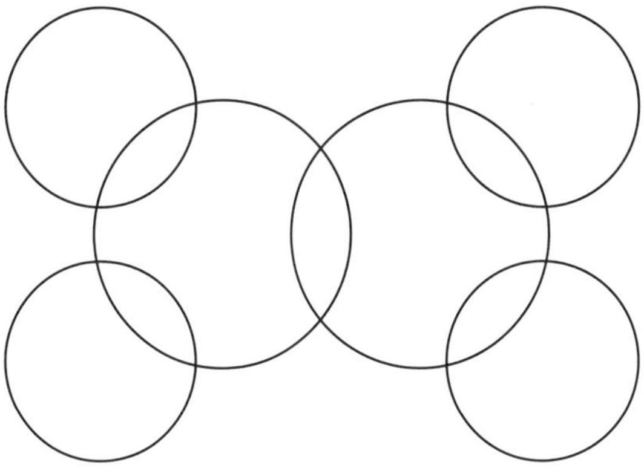

[3]

b) Ethane has the formula C_2H_6. In terms of electronic structure, explain why there is a single covalent bond between the two carbon atoms.

....

....

....

....

[4]

c) Describe the covalent bond that forms between a carbon atom and a hydrogen atom in terms of electrostatic attraction.

....

....

....

[2]

d) i) Calculate the M_r of ethane and ethene. Use the periodic table to help you.

M_r of ethane = ...　　　　　M_r of ethene = ...

[1]

ii) A student makes the following statement:
"The C=C double bond in ethene is stronger than the C–C single bond in ethane.
This means that ethene will have a higher boiling point than ethane."
Explain why the student's statement is incorrect.

....

....

....

....

[3]

[Total 13 marks]

Section 2 — The Periodic Table and Bonding

4   This question is about ionic compounds.

a) Magnesium chloride is formed from magnesium and chlorine.
    In terms of electron transfer, describe what happens when magnesium
    atoms react with chlorine atoms to form magnesium chloride.

    ....

    ....

    ....

    ....
                                                                                                        [3]

b) In general, the larger the charges on the ions in an ionic compound, the stronger the ionic bonds.
    Use this information to compare the melting point of magnesium oxide with the melting point of
    sodium chloride. Explain your answer.

    ....

    ....

    ....

    ....
                                                                                                        [3]

    Caesium chloride is an ionic compound with the chemical formula CsCl.

c) Give the formula of a caesium ion.
    Explain how it can be deduced from the chemical formula of caesium chloride.

    ....

    ....

    ....
                                                                                                        [2]

d) Draw a dot and cross diagram to show the bonding in caesium chloride.
    Only show the outer electrons. You should include the charges on the ions in your diagram.

                                                                                                        [2]

e) Write a balanced symbol equation, including state symbols,
    for the formation of caesium chloride from its elements.

    ....
                                                                                                        [2]
                                                                                          [Total 12 marks]

Section 2 — The Periodic Table and Bonding

5 The diagrams show the structures of diamond and silicon dioxide.

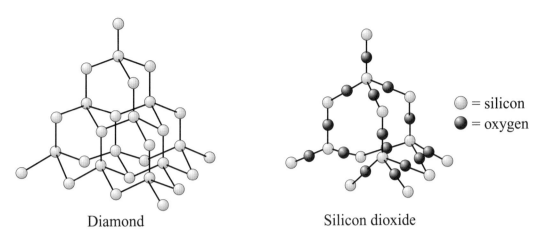

Diamond   Silicon dioxide

◯ = silicon
● = oxygen

a) Use the diagrams and your own knowledge of the bonding in diamond to give
   one similarity and **one** difference between the structures of diamond and silicon dioxide.

   ....

   ....

   ....
   [2]

b) Diamond is an extremely hard substance. State whether you would expect silicon dioxide to be a
   hard substance like diamond. Explain your answer.

   ....

   ....
   [2]

Graphite is a form of the element carbon.
The diagram shows the structure of graphite.

c) Use the diagram and your knowledge of graphite to explain why it is soft and slippery.

   ....

   ....

   ....
   [3]

   [Total 7 marks]

Exam Practice Tip

If you're stuck on a question about the structure of a substance, think about the type of bonding it
has and whether it will be a solid, liquid or gas. Alternatively, try using any known properties of the
substance (e.g. melting point) to give you an extra clue about its structure and bonding.

Score:

42

Section 2 — The Periodic Table and Bonding

Moles, Equations and Formulae

1 Calcium oxide (CaO) is produced by strongly heating calcium carbonate ($CaCO_3$).
Carbon dioxide (CO_2) is the only other product of this reaction.

a) 19.8 g of CO_2 was produced by heating a sample of calcium carbonate.
Calculate the mass of CaO that was also produced by this reaction.
Relative atomic masses (A_r): C = 12, O = 16, Ca = 40

Mass = ... g
[4]

Calcium oxide reacts with phosphorus pentoxide to form a single product, calcium phosphate(V).

b) A sample of calcium phosphate(V) was analysed.
It was found to contain 30.0 g of calcium, 15.5 g of phosphorus and 32.0 g of oxygen.
Use this information to deduce the empirical formula of calcium phosphate(V).
Relative atomic masses (A_r): O = 16, P = 31, Ca = 40

Empirical formula of calcium phosphate(V) = ...
[3]

c) Explain how the empirical formula of a compound differs from its molecular formula.

....

....

....
[2]

d) The empirical formula of phosphorus pentoxide is P_2O_5, and its relative formula mass is 284.
Use this information to deduce the chemical formula of phosphorus pentoxide.
Relative atomic masses (A_r): O = 16, P = 31

Chemical formula of phosphorus pentoxide = ...
[3]

[Total 12 marks]

2 "Fizzy sherbet" contains citric acid ($C_6H_8O_7$) and sodium hydrogencarbonate ($NaHCO_3$). When water is added to fizzy sherbet, the citric acid and the sodium hydrogencarbonate react to form carbon dioxide, water and sodium citrate ($C_6H_5O_7Na_3$).

The equation for this reaction is:

$$C_6H_8O_{7(s)} + 3NaHCO_{3(s)} \rightarrow 3CO_{2(g)} + 3H_2O_{(l)} + C_6H_5O_7Na_{3(aq)}$$

A student tested two brands of fizzy sherbet by mixing 10 g of each type with water in an open flask. She measured the mass of each flask and its contents at the start and end of the reaction.

a) Explain why a decrease in mass was expected.

....

....
[1]

b) The student tested the pH of the colourless solution in each flask at the end of the experiment.
She concluded that unreacted citric acid was present in one of the flasks.
State which of the reactants limited the amount of product formed in this case.
Explain your answer.

....

....
[1]

c) The student decided to make her own fizzy sherbet using 20.0 g of citric acid.
Calculate the minimum mass of sodium hydrogencarbonate needed to ensure all of the citric acid is used up in the reaction. Give your answer to three significant figures.
Relative formula masses (M_r): $NaHCO_3 = 84$; $C_6H_8O_7 = 192$

Mass = ... g
[3]

d) Another student repeated the reaction between citric acid and sodium hydrogencarbonate, but used different quantities of reactants. At the end of the reaction the water was evaporated and a 61.15 g sample of sodium citrate was collected. Use the reaction equation to calculate the mass of citric acid that reacted. Give your answer to three significant figures.
Relative formula mass (M_r) of $C_6H_8O_7 = 192$
Relative atomic masses (A_r): $H = 1$; $C = 12$; $O = 16$; $Na = 23$

Mass = ... g
[3]
[Total 8 marks]

3   Sucrose has the chemical formula $C_{12}H_{22}O_{11}$. Sucrose can react as follows:

Equation 1: $C_{12}H_{22}O_{11} + 12O_2 \rightarrow 12CO_2 + 11H_2O$ (complete combustion)

Equation 2: $C_{12}H_{22}O_{11} + nO_2 \rightarrow xCO + yCO_2 + 11H_2O$ (incomplete combustion)

Equation 3: $C_{12}H_{22}O_{11} \rightarrow 12C + 11H_2O$ (decomposition)

Relative formula masses (M_r): $C_{12}H_{22}O_{11} = 342$; $CO_2 = 44$; $CO = 28$; $H_2O = 18$;
Relative atomic mass (A_r) of $C = 12$

a) Use **Equation 1** to calculate the number of moles of carbon dioxide that will be produced from the complete combustion of 6.84 g of sucrose.

☐ **A** 10.56 moles of carbon dioxide

☐ **B** 44 moles of carbon dioxide

☐ **C** 0.24 moles of carbon dioxide

☐ **D** 6.84 moles of carbon dioxide

[1]

b) A student heats 5.13 g of sucrose in a sealed container to ensure incomplete combustion. 3.36 g of CO and 2.64 g of CO_2 are produced. Calculate the number of moles of CO and CO_2 produced and use your answers to write **Equation 2** as a balanced equation.

Balanced symbol equation: $C_{12}H_{22}O_{11} +$ ....$O_2 \rightarrow$ .... $CO +$ .... $CO_2 + 11H_2O$

[3]

c) Another student strongly heats a sample of sucrose until a black residue of carbon remains. Use **Equation 3** to calculate the mass of carbon produced from 12.0 g of sucrose. Give your answer to three significant figures.

Mass = ... g

[3]

[Total 7 marks]

Section 3 — Equations, Calculations and Electrolysis

4 A student makes hydrated copper sulfate crystals via the three-step process shown below.

> **Step 1**: Heat copper carbonate until it forms copper oxide.
>
> $$CuCO_{3(s)} \rightarrow CuO_{(s)} + CO_{2(g)}$$
>
> **Step 2**: Add an excess of copper oxide to sulfuric acid until all the acid has reacted.
>
> $$CuO_{(s)} + H_2SO_{4(aq)} \rightarrow CuSO_{4(aq)} + H_2O_{(l)}$$
>
> **Step 3**: Filter the solution and heat the filtrate until most of the water has evaporated. Leave the remaining water to evaporate until crystallisation occurs.

Relative formula masses (M_r): $CuO = 79.5$; $H_2SO_4 = 98$; $CuSO_4 = 159.5$; $H_2O = 18$.

a) 12.0 g of $CuCO_3$ is used in **Step 1**. At the end of **Step 1** the mass of the CuO is 5.10 g. Calculate the percentage yield of copper oxide. Give your answer to three significant figures. Relative atomic masses (A_r): $C = 12$; $O = 16$; $Cu = 63.5$

Percentage yield = ... %

[5]

The formula for hydrated copper sulfate crystals can be written as $CuSO_4.xH_2O$, where x is the number of moles of water for each mole of copper sulfate.

b) By repeating the process, the student manages to obtain 34.9 g of hydrated copper sulfate crystals. After heating these crystals in a crucible, the student is left with 22.3 g of anhydrous copper sulfate crystals. Use this information to calculate the value of x in the formula $CuSO_4.xH_2O$.

$x =$ ....

[4]

[Total 9 marks]

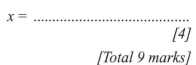

Exam Practice Tip

If you're given the mass of something and its relative formula or atomic mass (M_r or A_r), you should always try to calculate the number of moles. It's a good way to start a question if you're finding it difficult and it's usually worth a mark or two — even if you don't quite get to the final answer.

Score:

36

Gases and Concentrations

1 A student carries out an experiment to find the volume of sulfuric acid required to neutralise a potassium carbonate solution. The equation for the reaction is:

$$K_2CO_{3\,(aq)} + H_2SO_{4\,(aq)} \rightarrow K_2SO_{4\,(aq)} + H_2O_{(l)} + CO_{2\,(g)}$$

The student uses a pipette to add 25.0 cm³ of potassium carbonate solution to a conical flask, then adds an indicator. The reaction requires 22.5 cm³ of 2.00 mol/dm³ sulfuric acid for neutralisation.

a) Calculate the concentration of the potassium carbonate solution in mol/dm³.
Give your answer to three significant figures.

Concentration = ... mol/dm³

[2]

b) A different potassium carbonate solution has a concentration of 2.00 mol/dm³.
This solution was made by dissolving some solid potassium carbonate in 25 cm³ of water.
Calculate the mass of potassium carbonate dissolved in the solution.
Relative formula mass (M_r) of K_2CO_3 = 138

Mass = ... g

[2]

c) The student carries out the same reaction, but this time collects the gas that is produced.
She uses a solution containing 0.552 g of potassium carbonate and an excess of sulfuric acid, at room temperature and pressure.
Calculate the volume, in cm³, of carbon dioxide gas that is produced.
The volume of one mole of gas at room temperature and pressure is 24.0 dm³.

Volume = ... cm³

[3]

d) The student makes 25.0 cm³ of 234.6 g/dm³ potassium carbonate solution. Calculate the volume of 2.00 mol/dm³ sulfuric acid required to neutralise the potassium carbonate solution. Give your answer in cm³ and to three significant figures.

Volume = ... cm³

[4]

[Total 11 marks]

2   The equation for the decomposition of hydrogen peroxide is:

$$2H_2O_{2\,(aq)} \rightarrow 2H_2O_{(l)} + O_{2\,(g)}$$

a) The decomposition is carried out at room temperature and pressure, using potassium iodide as a catalyst. 60 cm³ of oxygen gas is produced. Calculate the number of moles of oxygen gas produced. The volume of one mole of gas at room temperature and pressure is 24.0 dm³.

.... mol

[1]

b) The hydrogen peroxide solution contains 60 g of hydrogen peroxide per 1 dm³. Calculate the maximum volume of oxygen gas that could be obtained from 100 cm³ of hydrogen peroxide. Give your answer in dm³ and to two significant figures. The volume of one mole of gas at room temperature and pressure is 24.0 dm³. Relative formula mass (M_r) of H_2O_2 = 34

Volume = ... dm³

[4]

[Total 5 marks]

Exam Practice Tip

Practice makes perfect when it comes to these sorts of calculations. Make sure you're familiar with the volume and concentration formula triangle, as well as the one for mass and moles. Looking at the units carefully in each question may also help you understand what you need to do at each step.

Score:

16

Section 3 — Equations, Calculations and Electrolysis

Paper 2

Electrolysis

1 What are the products of the electrolysis of magnesium chloride solution?

		Product at cathode	**Product at anode**
☐	**A**	Hydrogen	Oxygen
☐	**B**	Hydrogen	Chlorine
☐	**C**	Magnesium	Oxygen
☐	**D**	Magnesium	Chlorine

[Total 1 mark]

2 Sodium can be extracted from molten sodium bromide using electrolysis.

a) Describe the movement of ions in an electrolytic cell.
You should mention the different electrodes in your answer.

....

....

....

[2]

b) Using your knowledge of electrolysis, predict the redox processes in the sodium bromide
electrolytic cell. Include relevant ionic half-equations in your answer.

....

....

....

....

....

....

[4]

c) Explain why this electrolysis is carried out using molten sodium bromide,
rather than aqueous sodium bromide.

....

....

....

....

....

[4]

[Total 10 marks]

Section 3 — Equations, Calculations and Electrolysis

Paper 2

3 A cell is constructed using an electrolyte and inert graphite electrodes.
Gaseous products are formed at both the anode and the cathode.

a) Which of the following electrolytes could **not** have been used in the cell?

  ☐ **A** Molten zinc chloride

  ☐ **B** Dilute hydrochloric acid

  ☐ **C** Aqueous potassium chloride

  ☐ **D** Aqueous sodium chloride

[1]

b) State why the electrodes used in electrolysis are usually made from an inert material.

....

....

[1]

[Total 2 marks]

4 The table shows the products formed when the ionic compound **X**
is electrolysed as both an aqueous solution and a molten electrolyte.

Electrolyte	Product at cathode	Product at anode
Aqueous solution of **X**	Hydrogen gas (H_2)	Oxygen gas (O_2) and water (H_2O)
Molten **X**	A solid layer of pure potassium (K)	Oxygen gas (O_2) and water (H_2O)

a) Suggest the identity of compound **X**.

....

[1]

b) Write ionic half-equations for the oxidation and reduction processes during the electrolysis of an
aqueous solution of compound **X**.

Oxidation: ....

Reduction: ....

[2]

c) Explain why hydrogen gas is formed at the cathode during
the electrolysis of an aqueous solution of compound **X**.

....

....

[2]

[Total 5 marks]

Exam Practice Tip

Ionic half-equations crop up quite a bit in electrolysis, so you need to be confident at writing them.
Remember, just like in a full equation, you need the same atoms and equal charges on both sides
— but you should only have electrons on one side, showing a reactant being oxidised or reduced.

Score: ☐

18

Section 3 — Equations, Calculations and Electrolysis

Section 4 — Inorganic Chemistry

Alkali Metals and Halogens

1 This question is about the elements in Group 1 and Group 7 of the periodic table.

a) Predict the structure and bonding of elemental astatine. Explain your prediction.

Prediction: ....

Explanation: ....

....

[3]

b) Predict the physical state of elemental astatine at room temperature. Explain your answer.

....

....

[2]

c) Describe the reaction, if any, that you would expect to take place between astatine and aqueous sodium chloride. Explain your answer.

....

....

....

[2]

d) Rubidium and iodine are both in Period 5 of the periodic table.
Explain why rubidium is highly reactive but iodine has low reactivity.

....

....

....

....

[4]

[Total 11 marks]

2 Lithium and potassium are both Group 1 metals.

a) Predict what would happen to the mass of a sample of lithium if it was exposed to air for an extended period of time. Explain your answer.

....

....

....

[2]

b) Write a balanced symbol equation for the reaction of lithium with water. Include state symbols.

....

[3]

Paper 2

c) Lithium and potassium both react with water. Describe **one** similarity and **one** difference in what would be observed during these reactions. Explain your answers.

....

....

....

....

....

....

[4]

[Total 9 marks]

3   A student adds chlorine water to a solution of sodium iodide.

a) Predict what the student would observe. Explain your answer.

....

....

....

[3]

b) i) Explain what is meant by a redox reaction.

....

....

[1]

ii) Describe the redox processes in the reaction observed by the student.

....

....

[2]

c) Predict how the student's observations would differ if they added chlorine water to sodium bromide and to sodium chloride instead. Explain your answer.

....

....

....

....

[4]

[Total 10 marks]

Exam Practice Tip

Make sure you can describe and explain the reactivity trends of both alkali metals and halogens. If you're stuck on a question about their reactions, try writing out the equation. Seeing it written down might help you work out what's going on — or even get you marks in some questions.

Score:

30

Section 4 — Inorganic Chemistry

Gases and Their Reactions

1   Some of the percentage compositions of the atmospheres of Earth
    and Venus are shown in the table below. The data is for dry air.

a) Complete the table by filling in the approximate percentage composition
   of nitrogen, oxygen and argon in Earth's atmosphere.

Percentage composition (%)	Nitrogen	Oxygen	Argon	Carbon dioxide
Earth				0.04
Venus	3.5	trace	trace	96.5

[2]

b) Venus has the highest average surface temperature of any planet in the Solar System.
   Use the data in the table above to suggest **one** reason why Venus is so much hotter than Earth.

....

....

....

....

....

....

[4]

[Total 6 marks]

2   Magnesium and sulfur both burn in oxygen.

A scientist burns one mole of magnesium in a sealed container.
One mole of sulfur is also burnt in an identical container holding the same volume of air.

Write a balanced symbol equation for each reaction, and use your equations to explain which
container would have the lower percentage of oxygen gas after complete combustion.

....

....

....

....

....

....

[Total 3 marks]

3 Calcium oxide can be produced by the combustion of pure calcium in air or by the thermal decomposition of calcium carbonate.

a) Draw a labelled diagram to show the experimental set-up that could be used to collect carbon dioxide from the thermal decomposition of calcium carbonate.

[3]

A scientist burnt pure calcium in a sealed container of air. She then used phosphorus to determine the percentage of oxygen in 50.0 cm^3 of air sampled from the container.

b) Describe how phosphorus can be used to determine the percentage of oxygen in a sample of air.

....

....

....

....

....

[4]

c) After the test with phosphorus, the volume of the sample of air was 39.5 cm^3. Calculate the percentage volume of oxygen in the air sample.

Percentage of oxygen in air sample = ... %

[1]

d) The scientist made the following statement:
"The container must not have been sealed properly during the combustion of calcium."
Explain how your answer to part c) supports the scientist's statement.

....

....

....

[2]

[Total 10 marks]

Exam Practice Tip

A good way to remember all the facts in this section might be to write out the information in different ways. For example, you could draw a pie chart to show the composition of Earth's atmosphere, or make a table showing the products and equations of different combustion reactions.

Score:

19

Section 4 — Inorganic Chemistry

Reactivity of Metals

1 Titanium and its alloys are useful materials due to their strength, low density and resistance to corrosion. However, their use is limited by the high cost of titanium extraction.

a) Use the reactivity series on the right to suggest why titanium is a suitable material for pipes that transport seawater.

....

....

Sodium
Calcium
Magnesium
Titanium
Iron
Copper

Increasing reactivity ↑

[1]

b) The most common ores of titanium are rutile, TiO_2, and ilmenite, $FeTiO_3$. Suggest **one** reason why it might be preferable to extract titanium from rutile, even though rutile is less abundant and more expensive than ilmenite.

....

[1]

The process for extracting titanium from rutile is shown below.

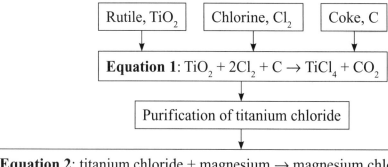

Rutile, TiO_2 Chlorine, Cl_2 Coke, C

Equation 1: $TiO_2 + 2Cl_2 + C \rightarrow TiCl_4 + CO_2$

Purification of titanium chloride

Equation 2: titanium chloride + magnesium → magnesium chloride + titanium

Electrolysis   Magnesium recycled

Equation 3: magnesium chloride → magnesium + chlorine

c) Use this information to suggest **two** reasons why the extraction of titanium is expensive.

1. ....

2. ....

[2]

d) Write a balanced symbol equation for **Equation 2**.

....

[2]

e) Explain why electrolysis is used to obtain magnesium from magnesium chloride, rather than reduction by carbon.

....

....

[1]

[Total 7 marks]

2 This question is about the reactivity of metals.

Zinc reacts with iron(II) chloride. The equation for the reaction is:

$$Zn + FeCl_2 \rightarrow ZnCl_2 + Fe$$

a) Predict what would occur if copper was used instead of zinc. Explain your answer.

....

....

[2]

b) State whether the zinc is oxidised or reduced. Write an ionic half-equation to show this.

....

....

[2]

c) When magnesium is added to blue copper sulfate solution ($CuSO_4$), a reaction occurs in which the colour of the solution fades and an orange-brown solid is formed on the magnesium. Write a balanced symbol equation for this reaction. Include state symbols. Use your equation to explain the observations made.

Equation: ....

Explanation: ....

....

....

[4]

d) Displacement reactions give out heat energy. Use the reactivity series to suggest why the amount of heat energy given out by the reaction between calcium and magnesium nitrate is very small.

....

....

[1]

e) The table shows the results of adding three different metals to water and to dilute acid.

Metal	X	Y	Z
Reaction with water	Slight fizzing	No reaction	Fizzing
Reaction with dilute acid	Fizzing	No reaction	Vigorous fizzing

Which of the following is true?

☐ **A** Metal X could displace metal Y from a solution of metal Y's salt

☐ **B** The order of reactivity is Y < Z < X

☐ **C** Metal Z is near the bottom of the reactivity series

☐ **D** Metal X will not react with steam

[1]

[Total 10 marks]

3 This question is about the properties of materials.

Part of the reactivity series of metals is shown.

Potassium
Sodium
Calcium
Magnesium
Zinc
Iron
Copper

Decreasing reactivity

a) The hull of a ship is made of steel and has magnesium blocks attached to it.
Use your knowledge and the reactivity series to explain the use of the magnesium blocks.
Include in your answer why magnesium is a good choice for the blocks.

....

....

....

....

....

[4]

b) Use your own knowledge and the reactivity series to suggest which of these metals
would be the most suitable material for hot water pipes in an underfloor heating system.

....

....

....

....

[3]

c) Give **three** physical properties that iron and copper have in common with aluminium.

1. ....

2. ....

3. ....

[3]

d) Aluminium has several uses that iron and copper would be unsuitable for.
Explain why aluminium is the most suitable of these three metals for making drinks cans.

....

....

....

[2]

[Total 12 marks]

Paper 2

4 This question is about alloys.

a) The main body of an aircraft is made of an alloy of aluminium that contains 4.5% copper, 0.6% manganese, 1.5% magnesium and 0.5% other elements. The total mass of the body is 68 500 kg.

i) Calculate the mass of aluminium it contains.

Mass = ... kg
[2]

ii) Magnesium is more lightweight than aluminium. Suggest why an alloy with a higher percentage of magnesium was not used to make the aircraft.

....

....
[2]

Steel alloys are made from iron and carbon, with other elements.
Stainless steels can contain chromium and nickel. They are hard and corrosion-resistant.

Paper 2

b) Explain why stainless steels are stronger than pure iron.

....

....

....

....
[3]

c) Suggest why low carbon steel is used to manufacture car bodies, despite stainless steels being more resistant to corrosion.

....

....
[1]

d) High carbon steel is strong and inflexible. It is often used to construct bridges. Suggest an explanation for why steel bridges are regularly repainted.

....

....

....
[2]

[Total 10 marks]

Exam Practice Tip

The reactivity series is a great tool for understanding the reactivity of metals, so make sure you know how to use it. By looking at the relative positions of metals and carbon, you can work out if a metal can be reduced by carbon and whether or not it will react with an aqueous salt of another metal.

Score: ___ / **39**

Acids and Their Reactions

1   An unknown mass of sodium hydroxide was used to make 25 cm³ of sodium hydroxide solution.
This solution was neutralised by 0.25 mol/dm³ hydrochloric acid in a titration.

a) The pH of the solution was measured throughout the titration. The results are shown on the graph.
Determine the volume of hydrochloric acid required to neutralise the sodium hydroxide solution.

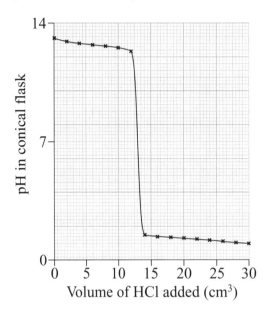

Volume = ... cm³

[1]

b) A different mass of sodium hydroxide was used to make another 25 cm³ solution.
35 cm³ of 0.25 mol/dm³ hydrochloric acid was required to neutralise this solution.
Calculate the mass of sodium hydroxide in the 25 cm³ solution that was used in the titration.
Relative formula mass (M_r) of NaOH = 40

Mass = ... g

[3]

c) Explain this neutralisation reaction in terms of proton transfer.

....

....

....

[2]

[Total 6 marks]

2 This question is about the reactions of acids.

a) Dilute hydrochloric acid is added to a flask containing an unknown solid substance.
A reaction occurs. The only products of the reaction are sodium chloride and hydrogen gas.

   i) Suggest the identity of the unknown solid substance.

   ....
   [1]

   ii) Describe how you could confirm the identity of the gas.

   ....

   ....

   ....
   [2]

b) A student has two flasks containing the same volume of 0.5 mol dm^{-3} nitric acid, HNO_3.
She adds some magnesium hydroxide to the first flask and the same mass of magnesium
carbonate to the second flask.

   i) Write a balanced equation for the reaction between magnesium hydroxide and nitric acid.

   ....
   [2]

   ii) State and explain **one** difference that the student will observe between the two reactions.

   ....

   ....

   ....
   [2]

   iii) Give **one** other reagent that the student could have added to the first flask
   instead of magnesium hydroxide that would produce the same two products.

   ....
   [1]

c) Another student has a solid metal compound, **MX**. He adds a sample of **MX** to
a beaker of deionised water and stirs. No solid residue can be seen in the beaker.

   The student then measures the pH of a solution of sulfuric acid. He adds a sample of solid
   MX to the sulfuric acid. The pH of the solution increases. No bubbles are produced.
   State and explain what this tells you about the nature of the metal compound, **MX**.

   ....

   ....

   ....

   ....

   ....
   [4]

   [Total 12 marks]

Section 4 — Inorganic Chemistry

3 Solutions of copper(II) sulfate and barium nitrate are mixed in a beaker to produce barium sulfate.

a) Describe what would be observed during the reaction. Explain your answer.

....

....

[2]

b) Describe how a pure, dry sample of barium sulfate could be obtained from the reaction mixture.

....

....

....

[3]

c) The other product of this reaction is copper(II) nitrate. State why a dry sample of copper(II) nitrate cannot be obtained in the same way as that of barium sulfate.

....

[1]

In another experiment, copper(II) nitrate, $Cu(NO_3)_2$, is produced by adding copper hydroxide, $Cu(OH)_2$, to nitric acid. After the reaction has taken place, excess solid copper hydroxide is removed by filtration.

d) Write a balanced symbol equation for this reaction. Include state symbols.

....

[3]

e) Describe how a pure, dry sample of copper(II) nitrate could be obtained from the filtered reaction mixture.

....

....

....

[3]

f) The exact amount of potassium hydroxide solution needed to neutralise a set amount of nitric acid can be determined by titration. Potassium nitrate solution is produced in the reaction.

i) Suggest **one** way the end point of the reaction between potassium hydroxide and nitric acid can be determined.

....

....

[1]

ii) Explain why it is important to determine the end point of the reaction before attempting to produce a potassium nitrate solution from this reaction.

....

....

[1]

[Total 14 marks]

Section 4 — Inorganic Chemistry

4 A student intends to use sulfuric acid of known concentration to determine the concentration of a sodium hydroxide solution.

The equation for the reaction is:

$$2NaOH_{(aq)} + H_2SO_{4(aq)} \rightarrow Na_2SO_{4(aq)} + 2H_2O_{(l)}$$

a) Describe a method the student could follow to determine the volume of the sodium hydroxide solution required to neutralise 25 cm³ of sulfuric acid.

....

....

....

....

[4]

The student carries out the experiment. The table shows his results.

Volume of NaOH solution (cm³)	Titration 1	Titration 2	Titration 3
Initial reading	0.00	21.50	0.20
Final reading	21.50	46.70	25.50
Volume added	21.50	25.20	25.30

b) What was the average volume of sodium hydroxide solution added? Ignore any anomalous results.

☐ **A** 24.0 cm³ ☐ **B** 24.00 cm³ ☐ **C** 25.25 cm³ ☐ **D** 25.30 cm³

[1]

c) In a second experiment, 23.40 cm³ of sodium hydroxide solution was required to neutralise 25.0 cm³ of 0.50 mol/dm³ sulfuric acid. Calculate the concentration of the sodium hydroxide solution in mol/dm³. Give your answer to three significant figures.

Concentration = ... mol/dm³

[3]

[Total 8 marks]

Exam Practice Tip

The more you understand the methods used to investigate reactions with acids, the easier they will be to remember — hopefully you'll get to try some out in class too. If you're asked about the solubility of a salt in the exam, try to remember whether it's one of the exceptions to the rules.

Score: ☐ / **40**

Chemical Tests

1   A student is given two bottles, each containing a colourless solution.
     The student is told that one bottle contains a solution of lithium chloride
     and the other contains a solution of potassium carbonate.

a)   The student is given access to the following:

   • A loop of platinum metal   • Silver nitrate solution
   • Dilute nitric acid   • A Bunsen burner
   • Dilute hydrochloric acid

   Devise a step-by-step method that the student could use to confirm
   both the cation and the anion present in each of the solutions.
   Include the expected results of each test and explain what they show.

   ....

   ....

   ....

   ....

   ....

   ....

   ....

   ....

                                                                                                                              [6]

b)   The student was given a third solution. This solution produced a sludgy green precipitate
     when mixed with sodium hydroxide solution. It produced a white precipitate when mixed with
     barium chloride solution. Give the chemical formula of the ionic compound in this solution.

     ....

                                                                                                                              [1]

                                                                                                                   [Total 7 marks]

2   The table shows the results of some chemical tests to identify two compounds.

Compound	A	$CaCl_2$
Flame Test	Yellow	B ....
Add dilute HCl	No visible change	C ....
Add dilute HNO_3 and $AgNO_3$ solution	Yellow precipitate	D ....

   Use your knowledge of the results of chemical tests to complete the table.

                                                                                                                   [Total 4 marks]

Section 4 — Inorganic Chemistry

3 This question is about chemical tests.

a) Sodium hydroxide solution was added to copper(II) sulfate solution. Describe what was observed.

....

....
[1]

Sodium hydroxide was added to an unknown solution. A strong smelling gas was given off.

b) Name this gas. Describe a test to confirm its identity.

....

....
[2]

c) Dilute hydrochloric acid was added to a fresh sample of the solution and another gas was given off. This gas was bubbled through limewater, which turned cloudy.

Suggest the chemical formula of the compound dissolved in the solution. Explain your answer.

....

....

....

....

....
[4]

d) Describe how copper(II) sulfate crystals can be used to test whether water is present in the unknown solution.

....

....

....

....
[3]

e) Further analysis showed that water was the main component of the unknown solution. The boiling point of the solution was found to be 101.5 °C. Explain this observation.

....

....

....
[2]

[Total 12 marks]

Exam Practice Tip

The results for ion tests are something you've just got to remember, but there are a couple of patterns that might help. As you go down the periodic table, the halides (chloride, bromide, iodide) produce a yellower precipitate with silver nitrate. See if you can spot any of your own patterns.

Score:

23

Section 4 — Inorganic Chemistry

Section 5 — Physical Chemistry

Energy Transfer

1   A student is investigating the temperature change of
    the reaction between sodium carbonate and citric acid.
    The table shows the results of the experiment.

This is the method used:
1.   Place 25 cm³ of sodium carbonate solution in a polystyrene cup.
2.   Measure the temperature of the solution.
3.   Add 1.2 g of citric acid, and stir the solution.
4.   Place a lid on the cup.
5.   When the reaction is complete, measure the temperature of the final solution.
6.   Repeat the experiment three times, and calculate the mean temperature change.
7.   Repeat the experiment, keeping all variables the same, except for the mass of citric acid.

Mass of citric acid added (g)	Mean temperature change (°C)
1.2	−0.3
3.2	−0.9
6.0	−1.4
7.5	−2.0
10.0	−2.5

a) Plot these results on the grid provided and draw a straight line of best fit.

[3]

Mass of citric acid added (g)

Temperature change (°C)

b) Predict the temperature change that would occur if 5 g of citric acid was added to
    the sodium carbonate solution. Show on your graph how you obtain your answer.

Temperature change = ... °C

[2]

c) Give **two** things the student has done to increase the validity of the results.
Explain your answers.

....

....

....

....

....

[4]

d) A scientist makes the following statement:
"The reaction of carbonate ions with acid is an endothermic reaction."
Explain this statement in terms of bond energies.

....

....

....

[2]

[Total 11 marks]

2 Nitrogen and hydrogen react together in the following way: $N_2 + 3H_2 \rightarrow 2NH_3$.

The overall enthalpy change of the reaction is –97 kJ/mol. The N≡N bond energy is 941 kJ/mol and the N–H bond energy is 391 kJ/mol. The displayed formula of NH_3 is shown.

H
|
N
H   H

a) Calculate the energy of the H–H bond.

H–H bond energy = ... kJ/mol

[4]

b) Use the information provided and your knowledge of bond energies
to explain why this reaction is exothermic.

....

....

....

[2]

[Total 6 marks]

Section 5 — Physical Chemistry

3   The diagram shows the energy change that occurs when methanol is burnt.

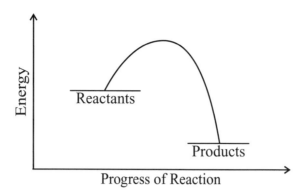

a) Use the diagram to explain why the combustion of methanol is an exothermic reaction.

....

....

....

                                                                                                             [2]

b) The combustion of 0.3 g of methanol produced an 8.9 °C rise in temperature in 25 g of water.
Calculate the heat energy transferred per gram of methanol, in kJ.
Give your answer to two significant figures.
$c = 4.2$ J/g/°C.

Heat energy transferred = ... kJ per gram

                                                                                                    [3]

c) In another experiment, 2.22 g of butanol, C_4H_9OH, was burnt to produce 80.1 kJ of heat energy.
Calculate the molar enthalpy change for the combustion of butanol, in kJ/mol.
Relative formula masses (A_r): H = 1; C = 12; O = 16

Molar enthalpy change = ... kJ/mol

                                                                                                  [4]

                                                                              [Total 9 marks]

Exam Practice Tip

When dealing with energy transfer questions, pay close attention to the number of bonds and molecules involved in the reaction. Also, be careful with positive and negative numbers if you have to rearrange the equation. The best thing to do is to get plenty of practice with these questions.

Score: ▢

26

Rates of Reaction

1   The equation for the reaction between sodium thiosulfate and hydrochloric acid is:

$$Na_2S_2O_{3(aq)} + 2HCl_{(aq)} \rightarrow 2NaCl_{(aq)} + S_{(s)} + SO_{2(g)} + H_2O_{(l)}$$

The diagram shows the experimental set-up a student used to investigate the rate of this reaction.

The student recorded the time taken for the cross to become obscured by a precipitate formed during the reaction. He repeated the experiment using five different concentrations of sodium thiosulfate solution.

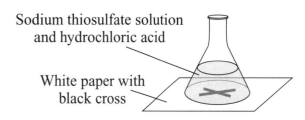

Sodium thiosulfate solution and hydrochloric acid

White paper with black cross

a) An anomalous result was identified. Which of the following would **not** explain the anomaly?

☐   **A**   Using different sized conical flasks for the experiments

☐   **B**   Using different sized measuring cylinders for the reactants

☐   **C**   Adding 20 ml of deionised water to the reaction mixture

☐   **D**   Using a lower concentration of HCl in the final experiment

[1]

This is the student's graph showing his results. The total volume of $Na_2S_2O_3$ solution and water was kept constant.

The student concluded that: "Doubling the concentration of $Na_2S_2O_3$ doubles the rate of reaction."

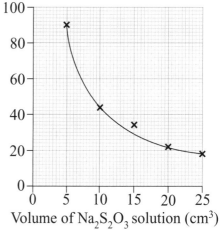

Time taken for cross to disappear (s)

Volume of $Na_2S_2O_3$ solution (cm³)

b) What evidence is there to support this conclusion? Use data from the graph in your answer.

....

....

....

[2]

c) Explain why doubling the concentration doubles the rate of reaction.
    Refer to particle collision theory in your answer.

....

....

[2]

d) Another student investigated the effect of temperature on the rate of the reaction between sodium thiosulfate and hydrochloric acid. Using your knowledge of collision theory, explain the effect of increasing the temperature on the reaction rate.

....

....

....

....

[4]

[Total 9 marks]

2   A student investigated the rate of reaction between marble chips and hydrochloric acid. The volume of carbon dioxide gas produced was measured at regular intervals until the reaction was complete.

The results are shown on the graph.

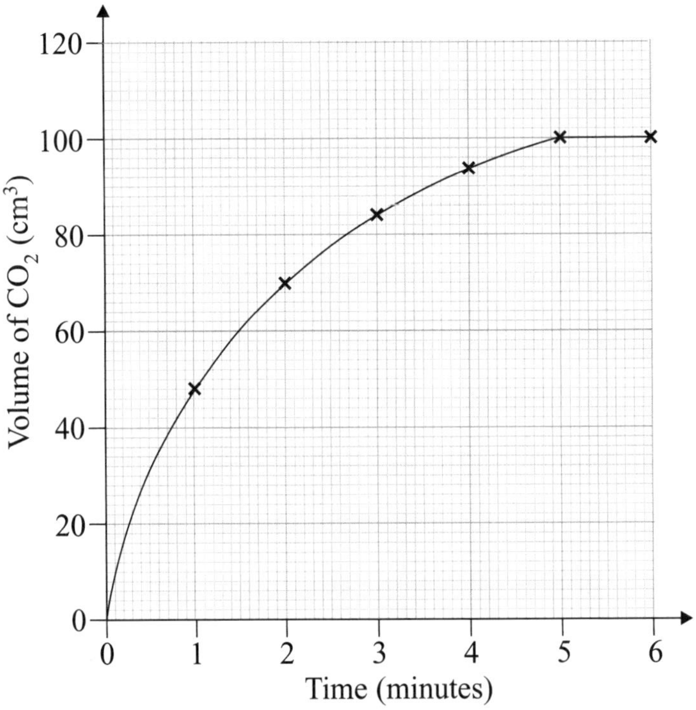

a) Calculate the rate of reaction at 3 minutes by drawing a tangent to the curve on the graph. Give your answer to two significant figures.

Rate of reaction = ... cm^3/min

[3]

b) The student concluded that, "The rate of reaction decreases with time." Explain how the data in the graph supports this conclusion.

....

....

....

[2]

c) The student repeated the experiment using crushed marble chips.
She found that the rate of reaction was too fast to measure the volume of gas accurately.
Which of the following changes to the method could she use to decrease the rate of this reaction?

A Place the conical flask in a bath of ice water

B Use a larger volume of hydrochloric acid

C Measure the volume of gas every 10 seconds

D Use a larger conical flask

[1]

[Total 6 marks]

3   The reaction between magnesium ribbon and excess hydrochloric acid produces hydrogen gas. The rate of reaction was investigated by measuring the mass of the reactants at regular intervals. The results are shown in the table.

Time (s)	0	10	20	30	40	50	60
Reactant Mass (g)	103.400	103.374	103.365	103.361	103.359	103.358	103.358

a) Plot a graph on the grid provided to show the loss in mass against time and draw a curved line of best fit.

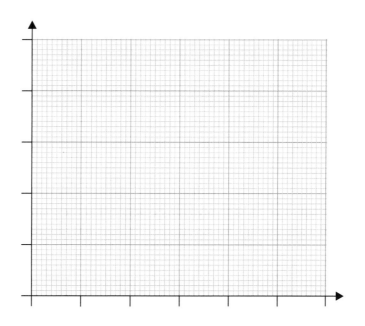

[5]

b) Use your graph to calculate the mean rate of reaction between 16 and 34 seconds.

Mean rate of reaction = ... g/s

[3]

[Total 8 marks]

Section 5 — Physical Chemistry

4   A student investigated the decomposition of hydrogen peroxide into water and oxygen using
     different masses of manganese(IV) oxide catalyst. The diagram shows the student's apparatus.

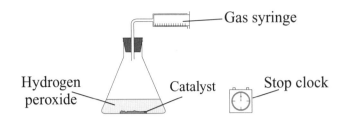

The student measured masses of powdered catalyst between 0.1 g and 0.7 g and
placed each into a conical flask containing 15 cm³ of hydrogen peroxide solution.
The student recorded the volume of gas produced in 60 seconds for each mass of catalyst.
None of the reactions went to completion within the 60 seconds.

a) Suggest the pattern that the student observed in her results. Explain your answer.

    ....

    ....
                                                                                                                [2]

b) The decomposition of hydrogen peroxide is exothermic. On a single set of axes, sketch and
    label **two** reaction profiles, to show the decomposition of hydrogen peroxide with and without a
    manganese(IV) oxide catalyst. Label the enthalpy change and activation energy on each profile.

                                                                                                                [4]

c) Describe a method that could be used to provide evidence that the manganese(IV) oxide behaved
    as a catalyst rather than a reactant in this reaction. Explain your answer.

    ....

    ....

    ....

    ....

    ....
                                                                                                                [3]
                                                                                              [Total 9 marks]

Exam Practice Tip

To calculate the rate of reaction at a certain point in time on a graph, you'll need to draw a tangent   **Score:**
to the curve. It's important to draw the tangent carefully — adjust your ruler until the space
between it and the curve is equal on both sides. Then just work out the gradient in the usual way.   **32**

Section 5 — Physical Chemistry

Reversible Reactions

1 Iodine monochloride is a dark brown liquid. It reacts with chlorine gas in a reversible reaction to produce a yellow solid, iodine trichloride.

The equation for the reaction is: $ICl_{(l)} + Cl_{2(g)} \rightleftharpoons ICl_{3(s)}$

a) Explain what happens when iodine monochloride reacts with chlorine gas in a closed system.

....

....

....

....

....

[4]

The diagram shows how the masses of iodine monochloride and iodine trichloride change with time.

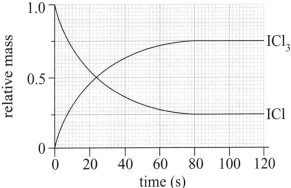

b) Determine the time at which equilibrium is reached.   Time = ... s

[1]

c) i) What would you observe if the pressure inside the closed system was decreased, but all other conditions remained the same?

☐ **A** More yellow solid and less dark brown liquid

☐ **B** More dark brown liquid and less yellow solid

☐ **C** No change in the quantities of dark brown liquid and yellow solid

☐ **D** More dark brown liquid and more yellow solid

[1]

ii) Explain your answer to part c) i) in terms of the position of equilibrium.

....

....

....

[2]

Paper 2

Section 5 — Physical Chemistry

d) A reaction tube containing iodine monochloride, chlorine gas and iodine trichloride was sealed and placed in an ice bath. The pressure was kept constant.
After a few seconds, the reaction mixture was found to contain more yellow solid.
Explain what this suggests about the forward reaction.

....

....

....

[3]

e) Explain what effect, if any, the addition of a catalyst would have on the yield of iodine monochloride. Assume all other conditions remain the same.

....

....

....

[3]

[Total 14 marks]

2 The Contact process is used for the manufacture of sulfuric acid.

The second stage in the process is a reversible reaction. The equation for this reaction is:

$$2SO_{2(g)} + O_{2(g)} \rightleftharpoons 2SO_{3(g)}$$

The graph shows how the percentage yield of sulfur trioxide (SO$_3$) changes with temperature.

Using this information and your own knowledge, describe how the percentage yield of SO$_3$ could be increased by:

Percentage yield of sulfur trioxide, SO$_3$ (%)

- changing the temperature at constant pressure
- changing the pressure at constant temperature

Explain your answers.

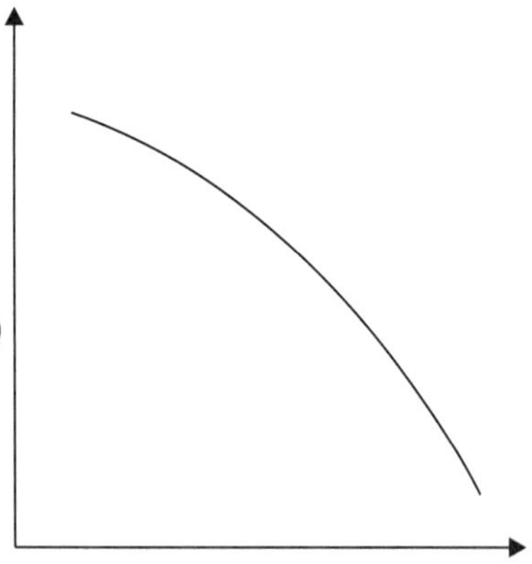

Temperature (°C)

Changing temperature: ....

....

....

Changing pressure: ....

....

....

[Total 4 marks]

Exam Practice Tip

If you're asked about a reversible reaction, pay close attention to the reaction equation. It can help you to figure out the effects of changing conditions, such as the pressure. And remember, dynamic equilibrium is only ever reached when the reaction is carried out in a closed system.

Score:

18

Organic Compounds and Crude Oil

1 Hydrocarbons from crude oil can be used to produce compounds such as poly(ethene).

The diagram represents a two-step process that produces poly(ethene). Hydrocarbon **A** has 10 carbon atoms. Its hot vapours are passed over a heated catalyst and hydrocarbons **B** and **C** are formed in a 1:1 ratio. Hydrocarbon **C** is used to produce the polymer poly(ethene).

Hydrocarbon A ⟶ Hydrocarbon B + Hydrocarbon C ↓ Poly(ethene)

a) Give the formulas of hydrocarbons **A**, **B** and **C**.

Hydrocarbon A: ....

Hydrocarbon B: ....

Hydrocarbon C: ....

[3]

b) Describe the properties of hydrocarbon **A** in comparison with those of the hydrocarbon $C_{35}H_{72}$. Explain why hydrocarbon **A** might be a more desirable product than $C_{35}H_{72}$.

....

....

....

....

....

....

....

....

....

[6]

c) Dodecane is a hydrocarbon with the formula $C_{12}H_{26}$. A reaction occurs when hot vapours of dodecane are passed over a heated catalyst. Hydrocarbon **C** and **one** other product are formed in the ratio 3:1. Write an equation to show this reaction.

....

[1]

[Total 10 marks]

44

2 This question is about burning hydrocarbons for fuel.

a) Petrol contains the hydrocarbon octane, which has eight carbon atoms.
Give the chemical formula of octane.

....

[1]

b) Write a balanced symbol equation for the combustion of octane in an excess of oxygen.

....

[2]

c) Solid particles of carbon, known as soot, can be formed when octane combusts
in a limited supply of oxygen. Various other products may also be produced.
Write a possible balanced symbol equation to show this.

....

[2]

d) Name the toxic gas that may also be produced by the incomplete combustion of hydrocarbons.
Describe how it can have an impact on human health.

....

....

....

....

[3]

e) Nitrogen gas is inert and does not react with oxygen in the air under normal circumstances.
Explain how burning hydrocarbons in car engines can create nitrogen oxides.

....

....

....

[2]

f) Describe how nitrogen oxides and sulfur dioxide from burning hydrocarbons may go on to cause
environmental damage.

....

....

....

....

[3]

[Total 13 marks]

Section 6 — Organic Chemistry

3 A student is studying organic compounds. He draws the four structures shown below.

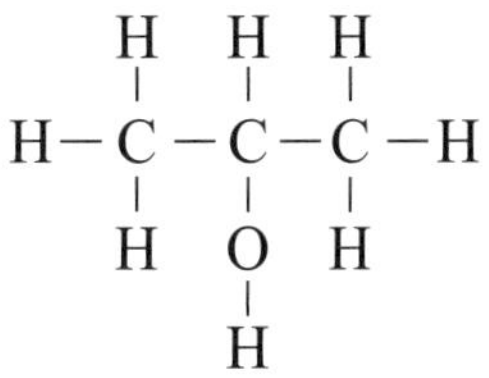

$$
\begin{array}{cccc}
\text{A} & \text{B} & \text{C} & \text{D}
\end{array}
$$

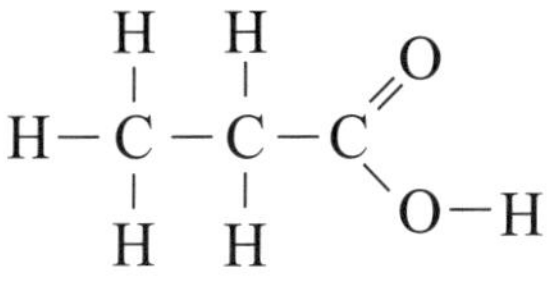

Structure A: H–C–C–C–H with H, H, H on top, H, O, H below, and an H below the O.

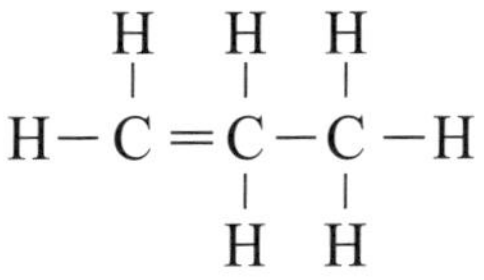

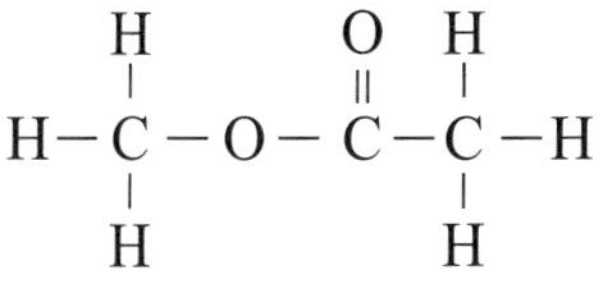

Structure B: H–C–C–C with H, H on top and H, H below, and the third C bonded to =O and O–H.

Structure C: H–C=C–C–H with H, H, H on top and H, H below.

Structure D: H–C–O–C–C–H with H on top of first C, O (double bond) and H on top, and H below first C, H below last C.

a) Which of the four structures has been drawn incorrectly?

☐ A ☐ B ☐ C ☐ D

[1]

b) Give the name of the hydrocarbon with the structural formula CH_3CHCH_2.

....

[1]

The student was asked to draw the structure of butene.
The student drew this structure:

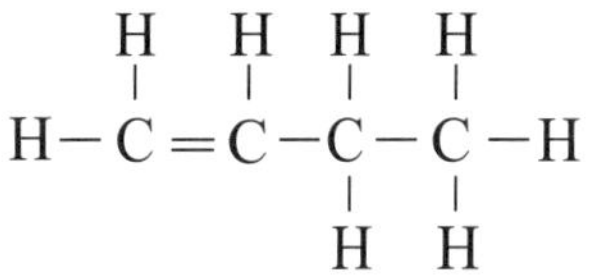

H–C=C–C–C–H with H, H, H, H on top and H, H below (on third and fourth carbons).

c) Draw an alternative structure for butene and explain
why the structure you have drawn is also correct.

....

....

[2]

d) The student made this statement about butene:

"The carbon atoms of butene share a double bond, so cannot bond to any more atoms.
This means that butene is saturated."

Explain whether or not the student's statement is correct.

....

....

....

[1]

[Total 5 marks]

Exam Practice Tip

Pay close attention to any information in the question — you could even underline the important
bits so that you can refer back to them quickly. You'll often need to apply your own knowledge to
some information you're given in order to work something out — just like in Q1b and 3d above.

Score: ☐
28

Section 6 — Organic Chemistry

Reactions of Organic Compounds

1 Simple hydrocarbons can be used to produce various different chemicals.

a) Suggest a two-step process that could be used to form propanoic acid from propene, by first producing an alcohol. Include any necessary reagents for each step.

Step 1: ....

Step 2: ....

[2]

b) Draw the displayed formula of propanoic acid.

[1]

c) Alkenes react with bromine water. During the reaction, the bromine water loses its orange colour. Use your knowledge of the reactions of alkenes to explain this observation.

....

....

....

....

[2]

Alkanes can be reacted with halogens to produce haloalkanes.
The diagram shows the structure of chloropropane:

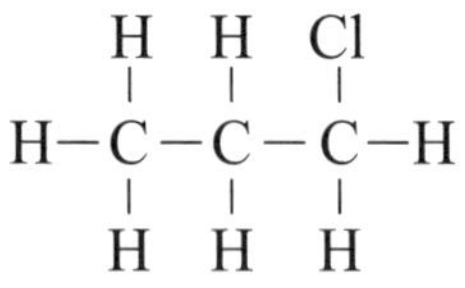

$$
\begin{array}{c}
\quad\ \text{H}\quad\ \text{H}\quad\ \text{Cl} \\
\quad\ | \quad\ | \quad\ | \\
\text{H}-\text{C}-\text{C}-\text{C}-\text{H} \\
\quad\ | \quad\ | \quad\ | \\
\quad\ \text{H}\quad\ \text{H}\quad\ \text{H}
\end{array}
$$

d) i) Write a symbol equation for the formation of chloropropane.

....

[2]

ii) Give the source of energy required for this reaction.

....

[1]

e) Explain why this type of reaction is known as a 'substitution reaction'.

....

....

[1]

[Total 9 marks]

2 Glycolic acid ($CH_2OHCOOH$) is a solid at room temperature. It is used as an ingredient in chemical face peels. The diagram shows the structure of glycolic acid.

$$
\begin{array}{c}
O \\
\diagdown \\
\quad C-C-O-H \\
H-O \quad
\end{array}
$$

with H above the second C, and H below the second C

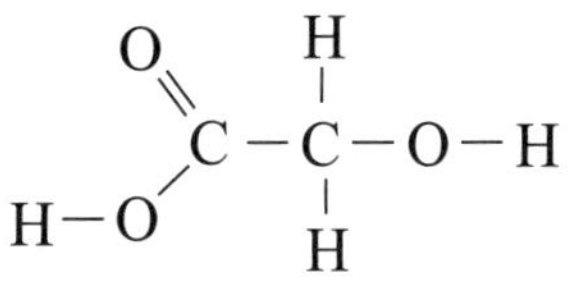

a) Suggest why glycolic acid undergoes reactions of **both** carboxylic acids and alcohols.

....

....

[1]

b) Describe what is observed when glycolic acid reacts with sodium carbonate solution (Na_2CO_3). Explain your answer. Include a balanced equation with state symbols.

....

....

....

....

....

[4]

c) Suggest what happens to the structure of glycolic acid when it reacts with an oxidising agent.

....

....

[1]

d) Explain how you could produce an ester from glycolic acid.

....

....

....

[2]

e) Draw the displayed formula of the ester that glycolic acid would form with another molecule of glycolic acid.

[1]

[Total 9 marks]

Section 6 — Organic Chemistry

3　The alcohol **X** has a straight carbon chain with an alcohol functional group on the end. The formula for alcohol **X** is C_4H_9OH.

a)　Draw the displayed formula of alcohol **X** and give its name.

....

[2]

b)　Give **two** methods by which alcohols can be oxidised to form carboxylic acids.

1. ....

2. ....

[2]

c)　Give the structural formula of the carboxylic acid produced by the oxidation of alcohol **X**.

....

[1]

d)　Alcohols such as **X** can be oxidised in another way that does not produce a carboxylic acid. Because of this reaction, alcohols like **X** can be used as fuels.

i)　Write a balanced symbol equation for this reaction.

....

[2]

ii)　Explain why this reaction means alcohols can be used as fuels.

....

....

[1]

e)　Ethanol (C_2H_5OH) is often described as a biofuel because it can be produced by living microorganisms. Describe how yeast cells are used to convert glucose into ethanol. Include the name of this process and the conditions in which it is carried out.

....

....

....

....

....

....

....

[5]

[Total 13 marks]

4 The diagram shows the structure of an ester being studied by a scientist.

a) Draw a circle around the functional group of the compound.

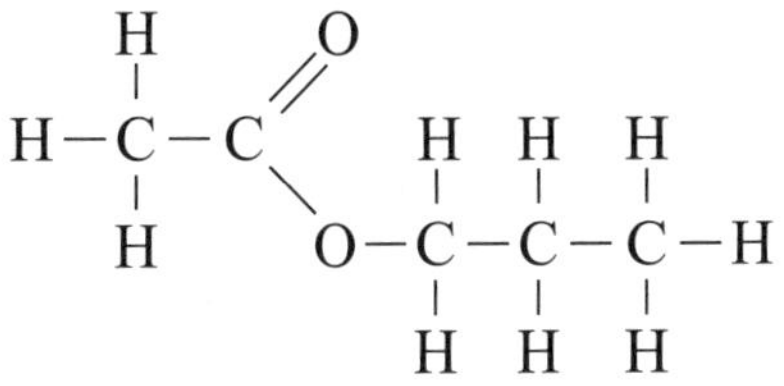

$$
\begin{array}{ccc}
 & H & O \\
 & | & \diagup\diagdown \\
H-C-C & & H \ \ H \ \ H \\
 & | & \diagdown | \ \ | \ \ | \\
 & H & O-C-C-C-H \\
 & & | \ \ | \ \ | \\
 & & H \ \ H \ \ H
\end{array}
$$

[1]

b) Esters are often used to add artificial smells or flavours to foods.
State and explain **two** typical properties of esters that make them suitable for this purpose.

....

....

....

....

[4]

c) Name the alcohol and carboxylic acid that react to form this compound.

Alcohol: ....

Carboxylic acid: ....

[2]

d) Write a balanced equation using structural formulae for the formation of this compound.

....

[3]

e) Describe a suitable method for producing this compound from an alcohol and a carboxylic acid.

....

....

....

....

....

....

....

....

[5]

[Total 15 marks]

Exam Practice Tip

You'll be expected to know the prefixes meth-, eth-, prop-, but-, pent- and hex- but you might also come across larger compounds or ones with special names in the exam. Unless you're told otherwise, assume that these undergo the same reactions as the ones you're familiar with.

Score:

46

Polymers

1   This question is about polymerisation reactions.

PCTFE is an addition polymer formed from chlorotrifluoroethene.
The diagrams show the structures of chlorotrifluoroethene and chlorotrifluoroethane.

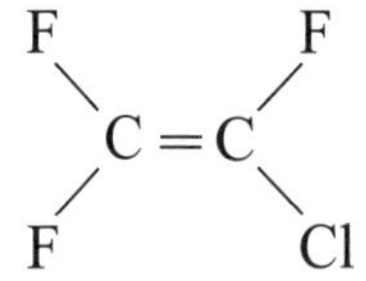

$$F\underset{F}{\overset{}{\diagdown}}C = C\underset{Cl}{\overset{F}{\diagup}}$$

chlorotrifluoroethene

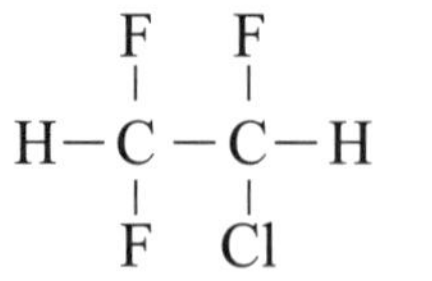

$$H-\underset{F}{\overset{F}{\underset{|}{C}}} - \underset{Cl}{\overset{F}{\underset{|}{C}}}-H$$

chlorotrifluoroethane

a) Explain why chlorotrifluoroethane cannot be used to produce PCTFE.

....

....

[2]

b) Draw a diagram to represent the formation of PCTFE from chlorotrifluoroethene.

[2]

The two monomers shown undergo a polymerisation reaction.

$$HO - \underset{H}{\overset{H}{\underset{|}{C}}} - \underset{H}{\overset{H}{\underset{|}{C}}} -OH \qquad HO-\overset{O}{\overset{||}{C}}-\underset{H}{\overset{H}{\underset{|}{C}}} - \underset{H}{\overset{H}{\underset{|}{C}}} - \underset{H}{\overset{H}{\underset{|}{C}}} - \underset{H}{\overset{H}{\underset{|}{C}}} - \underset{H}{\overset{H}{\underset{|}{C}}} - \underset{H}{\overset{H}{\underset{|}{C}}} - \overset{O}{\overset{||}{C}} -OH$$

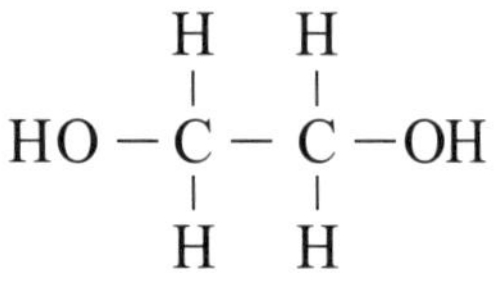

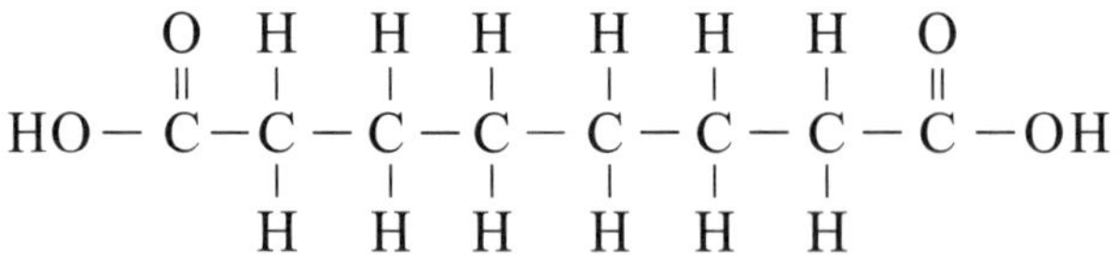

c) Name the type of polymerisation reaction that occurs. Describe what happens during the reaction.

Name: ....

Description: ....

....

[3]

d) Draw the structure of the polymer produced by this reaction.

[3]

[Total 10 marks]

Section 6 — Organic Chemistry

2 Addition polymers are used for a wide variety of purposes, despite the problems associated with disposing of them.

a) Discuss the reasons why addition polymers are difficult to dispose of.

....

....

....

....

....

[4]

b) Explain what is meant by 'biopolyesters' and why they may be a better choice than addition polymers for some purposes.

....

....

....

....

[3]

[Total 7 marks]

3 The polyester shown in the diagram is formed in a condensation reaction.

$$\left[\begin{array}{c} \\ -O-C-C-C-C-O-C-C-C- \\ \end{array} \right]_n$$

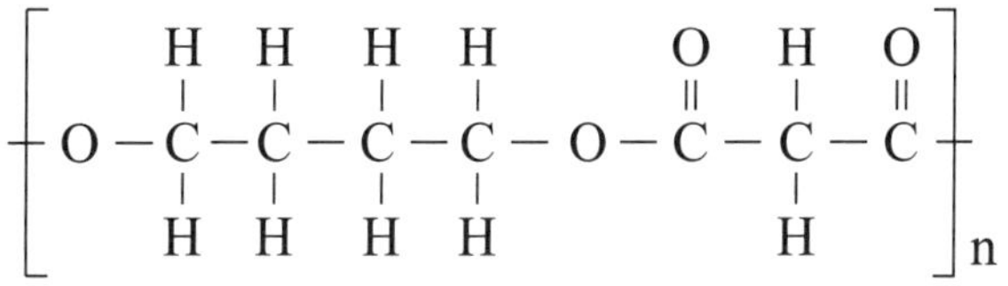

a) Which of the following pairs of monomers were the reactants in this reaction?

☐ **A** butanediol and propanoic acid

☐ **B** propanediol and butanedioic acid

☐ **C** butanediol and propanedioic acid

☐ **D** butanol and propanedioic acid

[1]

b) Water molecules are also formed during the condensation reaction. Give the ratio of repeating units : water molecules formed.

....

[1]

[Total 2 marks]

Exam Practice Tip

Make sure you know how many bonds an atom can form when you're drawing organic molecules. Remember: carbon forms 4 covalent bonds, oxygen forms 2, hydrogen and halogens can only form 1.

Score:

☐

19

 ☐   ☐ 😊 ☐

Mixed Questions for Paper 1

1   A scientist carried out a series of reactions to investigate the reactivity of two unknown elements, **A** and **Z**. His results are shown in the table below.

Reaction	Results
A with aqueous potassium iodide	Forms a brown solution containing a covalent compound and an ionic compound. An aqueous solution of this ionic compound reacts with Cl_2 to produce an orange solution.
A with **Z**	Forms a white solid, **X**, that dissolves in water.
Z with water	Vigorous reaction to form a metal hydroxide solution with a pH of 12. The metal hydroxide contains 69.64% **Z** by mass.

a) Identify element **A**. Explain your reasoning.

A = ...

Reasoning: ....

....

....

....

....

                                        [4]

b) Identify element **Z**. Explain your reasoning. Include any relevant calculations.

Z = ...

Reasoning: ....

....

....

....

....

                                          [4]

c) i) Give the formula of species **X**.

....

                                          [1]

ii) A solid sample of **X** does not conduct electricity.
Give **one** way the scientist could make **X** conduct electricity.

....

....

                                          [1]

                                      [Total 10 marks]

2 This question is about carbon dioxide.

a) The level of carbon dioxide in the atmosphere at the South Pole every ten years between 1960 and 2010 is shown in the table below. The values are rounded to the nearest 5 parts per million.

Year	1960	1970	1980	1990	2000	2010
CO_2 (parts per million)	315	325	335	350	365	385

i) Describe the trend in carbon dioxide levels shown in the table.

....

....

[2]

ii) Suggest the potential effect of this trend on the global mean sea level. Explain your answer.

....

....

....

....

....

....

[4]

b) Explain, in terms of structure and bonding, why carbon dioxide is a gas at room temperature but magnesium oxide is a solid.

....

....

....

....

....

....

....

[6]

c) When heated, calcium carbonate ($CaCO_3$) produces carbon dioxide and one other product.

i) What type of reaction is this?

....

[1]

ii) Describe how you could confirm that the gas produced by this reaction is carbon dioxide.

....

....

[2]

[Total 15 marks]

Mixed Questions for Paper 1

3 This question is about halogens and halide compounds.

a) Chlorine reacts with aqueous $FeCl_2$ to form $FeCl_3$ solution.

   i) Write a balanced chemical equation to show this reaction. Include state symbols.

   ....

   [2]

   ii) Explain, in terms of ions, why chlorine does not react with NaCl to form $NaCl_2$.

   ....

   ....

   ....

   [2]

b) A chemist places a glass lid over a beaker containing a few iodine crystals.
   She places an ice cube on top of the lid. She then gently heats the bottom of the beaker.
   Predict and explain what the chemist will observe inside the beaker.

   ....

   ....

   ....

   ....

   [4]

c) A scientist reacts a sample of bromine with a Group 1 element, **G**, to form a bromide compound.

   i) Describe and explain how bromine's bonding changes during this reaction.

   ....

   ....

   ....

   ....

   ....

   [4]

   ii) 20.00 g of bromine reacted to form 25.75 g of bromide compound.
   Identify element **G**. Show your working.
   $M_r(Br_2) = 160$

                                                        G = ...

   [5]

   [Total 17 marks]

4   A student adds some calcium carbonate (CaCO₃) chips to a flask containing dilute hydrochloric acid. She measures the volume of gas given off over the next 60 seconds.

a) Write a word equation for this reaction.

....

....

[1]

b) Identify the proton acceptor in this reaction.

....

[1]

c) The student repeats the experiment, but grinds the calcium carbonate into a powder before adding it to the acid. Predict the effect, if any, that this will have on the volume of gas given off in the first 60 seconds. Explain your answer. Assume that neither reaction is completed within 60 seconds.

....

....

....

....

....

[3]

d) The student adds excess calcium carbonate to the acid until all of the acid has reacted. Explain how the student could obtain a pure, dry sample of the salt produced by this reaction.

....

....

....

....

....

....

....

....

[6]

e) Explain why the method you described in part **d)** would not be suitable if calcium hydroxide had been used instead of calcium carbonate.

....

....

....

[2]

[Total 13 marks]

5 This question is about Group 0 elements.

Predict the boiling point of krypton using the data in the table on the right. Explain your reasoning. In your answer, refer to the structure and bonding of Group 0 elements.

Element	Boiling point (°C)
neon	–246
argon	–186
xenon	–108

....

....

....

....

....

....

[Total 5 marks]

6 Pentane (C_5H_{12}) is an alkane.

a) Name a process that can be used to produce pentane from long-chain hydrocarbons. Describe this process. Include any necessary conditions.

....

....

....

....

[4]

A student has 200 g of water in a beaker. He burns 0.50 g of pentane in a spirit burner beneath the beaker. The temperature of the water increases to 50.4 °C.

b) The student determines a molar enthalpy change of –3495 kJ/mol for the combustion of pentane. Calculate the initial temperature of the water. Give your answer to 3 significant figures. The specific heat capacity of water is 4.2 J/g/°C

temperature = ... °C

[5]

[Total 9 marks]

Mixed Questions for Paper 1

7 This question is about iron and its compounds.

a) An iron nail is weighed before being placed in an open beaker of water. After a long period, the nail is removed from the water, dried and reweighed. It is found that the mass of the nail has increased. Explain this observation.

....

....

[2]

b) Suggest why iron nails used in garden sheds are often coated in zinc. Explain your answer.

....

....

....

....

[4]

c) Describe how the presence of iron(II) ions in a solution could be determined chemically. Name the compound that would form during the chemical test.

....

....

....

[3]

d) Iron can be extracted from iron oxide using a blast furnace.
In the blast furnace, iron oxide reacts with carbon monoxide to form iron and carbon dioxide.

i) Name this type of reaction.

....

[1]

ii) 1.62 kg of an iron oxide was converted to 1.26 kg of iron in a blast furnace.
Use this information to determine the empirical formula of the iron oxide.

empirical formula = ...

[3]

[Total 13 marks]

Exam Practice Tip

Always show your working in calculation questions — even if you're pretty confident you know the answer. It's very easy to make a mistake if you start skipping steps here, there and everywhere, so take your time and write it all out. Even if it goes wrong, you'll probably still pick up some marks.

Score:

82

Mixed Questions for Paper 1

Mixed Questions for Paper 2

1 A copper sulfate solution was electrolysed using inert graphite electrodes. A deposit of copper metal was formed at the negative electrode. Bubbles were observed at the positive electrode.

a) i) Suggest the identity of the gas formed at the positive electrode.
Explain how this gas is formed.

....

....
[2]

ii) Write an ionic half-equation to show how this gas is formed.

....
[2]

iii) Describe a chemical test that would confirm the identity of the gas.

....

....
[2]

b) Some magnesium chloride solution was added to the copper sulfate solution.

i) State the products that will now be discharged at each electrode.
Explain your answers.

....

....

....

....

....

....
[4]

ii) Write an ionic half-equation for the reaction that occurs at the negative electrode.

....
[1]

c) Explain why adding silver chloride to the copper sulfate solution
has no effect on the products discharged at the anode and cathode.

....

....

....
[2]

[Total 13 marks]

2   Zinc can be extracted from the ore sphalerite, which contains zinc sulfide (ZnS).

Two of the steps are:

Step 1: Oxidation of zinc sulfide to produce zinc oxide (ZnO) and sulfur dioxide.

Step 2: Reduction of zinc oxide by carbon to produce zinc and carbon dioxide.

a) Write a balanced chemical equation for each of these steps. State symbols are not required.

1. ....

2. ....

[2]

b) Sulfur dioxide is a waste product of this process.

i)   Suggest why sulfur dioxide in the atmosphere can have a negative impact on aquatic species.

....

....

[2]

The waste sulfur dioxide can be used to produce sulfuric acid.

ii) The equation for the reaction is:

$$2SO_2 + 2H_2O + O_2 \rightarrow 2H_2SO_4$$

The structures of SO_2 and H_2SO_4 are given below.
The bond energies are shown in the table on the right.

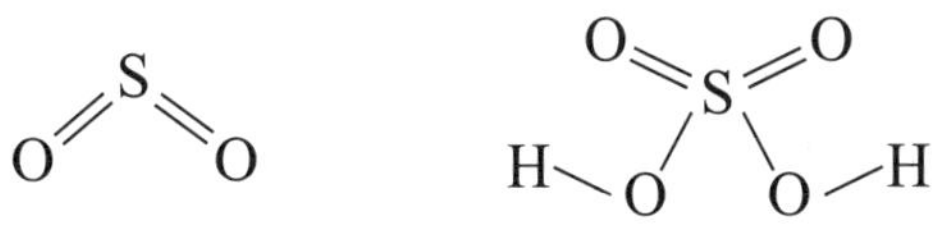

Bond	Energy (kJ/mol)
S = O	522
O = O	494
O – H	459
S – O	265

Calculate the enthalpy change of the reaction.

Enthalpy change = ... kJ/mol

[3]

iii) Draw a reaction profile for this reaction. Label the activation energy.

[4]

[Total 11 marks]

3   A student is investigating the reactions of Group 2 metals and their compounds.
    He adds some magnesium to 50 cm³ of 1.0 mol/dm³ hydrochloric acid.
    Both reactants are completely used up in the reaction.

The equation for the reaction is:

$$Mg_{(s)} + 2HCl_{(aq)} \rightarrow MgCl_{2(aq)} + H_{2(g)}$$

a) Calculate the volume of hydrogen produced by this reaction at room temperature and pressure.
    The volume of one mole of any gas at room temperature and pressure is 24.0 dm³.

Volume = ... dm³

[3]

b) The student repeated the experiment but replaced the magnesium with the same mass of calcium.
    Predict the effect on the amount of hydrogen produced. Explain your answer.

    ....

    ....

    ....

[3]

c) After the reaction with calcium was complete, 0.020 mol of hydrochloric acid remained in the
    solution. Calculate the volume of 0.65 mol/dm³ Ba(OH)$_2$ solution required to neutralise the
    remaining hydrochloric acid. Give your answer in cm³ and to two significant figures.

Volume = ... cm³

[4]

d) The student then reacted Mg(OH)$_2$ with HCl. MgCl$_2$ was produced with a 60% yield.
    Calculate the mass of Mg(OH)$_2$ required to produce 12.5 g of MgCl$_2$.
    Relative formula masses (M_r): MgCl$_2$ = 95, Mg(OH)$_2$ = 58

Mass = ... g

[5]

[Total 15 marks]

Mixed Questions for Paper 2

4 This question is about the compounds of calcium and copper.

a) Suggest **two** substances that will react together to produce calcium propanoate.

....

[1]

b) Give **one** way you could confirm the presence of Cu^{2+} ions in a compound.

....

....

....

[2]

c) A student wants to make a sample of copper carbonate.
She has access to deionised water, standard laboratory equipment and the following substances:

- copper hydroxide powder
- potassium carbonate powder
- copper chloride powder
- calcium carbonate powder

i) Identify the **two** substances from the list above that the student will
need to produce a sample of copper carbonate. Explain your answer.

Substances: ....

Explanation: ....

....

....

....

[4]

ii) Describe how the student can use the reactants you chose in
part **i)** to make a pure, dry sample of copper carbonate.

....

....

....

....

....

....

....

....

[5]

[Total 12 marks]

5 The Haber process is used to produce ammonia on an industrial scale.

The equation for the reaction is:

$$N_{2(g)} + 3H_{2(g)} \rightleftharpoons 2NH_{3(g)} \qquad \Delta H = -92 \text{ kJ/mol}$$

The ammonia formed in the reaction is removed by cooling the mixture of gases.
The remaining nitrogen and hydrogen are recycled.

a) What does this suggest about the boiling point of ammonia compared to the other two gases?

....

[1]

The graph below shows how temperature and pressure
affect the percentage yield of ammonia at equilibrium.

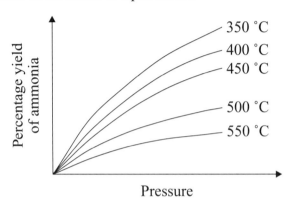

b) Explain how the percentage yield varies with pressure when the temperature remains at 550 °C.

....

....

....

....

[3]

c) Explain how the percentage yield is affected as the temperature increases at a constant pressure.

....

....

....

....

[3]

d) The Haber process uses an iron catalyst. Which of the following statements is true?

☐ **A** The iron catalyst increases the percentage yield of the reaction.

☐ **B** The iron catalyst increases the rate of both the forward and backward reactions.

☐ **C** The iron catalyst removes the activation energy.

☐ **D** The iron catalyst changes the position of the equilibrium.

[1]

[Total 8 marks]

6 The diagram below shows a reaction scheme involving some organic compounds.

$$\text{Ethanol} \xrightarrow{\hspace{1.5cm}} \text{Ethanoic acid} \xrightarrow[\text{Acid, } \mathbf{A}]{\text{Ethanol}} \mathbf{X}$$

a) Name a suitable oxidising agent for the oxidation of ethanol to ethanoic acid.

....
[1]

b) Draw the structure of compound **X**. Give its name.

Name = ...
[2]

c) State the role of acid **A**. Explain its effect on the reaction.

....

....

....
[3]

d) Ethanoic acid will react with potassium.

  i) Write a balanced chemical equation for this reaction.

....
[2]

  ii) Name the potassium-containing product.

....
[1]

  iii) Ethanoic acid will also react with sodium. Explain, in terms of electrons, why you
  would expect this reaction to occur more slowly than the reaction with potassium.
  Assume all variables apart from the identity of the metal are kept the same.

....

....

....

....
[3]

[Total 12 marks]

Exam Practice Tip

The questions in your exams won't just stick to one topic, so don't get caught out. Just because
a question starts off by asking you about alcohols doesn't mean the whole of that question will be
about alcohols. You need to be prepared to think across all of the relevant content for your paper.

Score: ⬜
_____
71

Answers

Answers

Section 1 — Particles and Mixtures

Pages 1-2 — States of Matter

1 a) When liquid bromine is heated, its particles gain energy *[1 mark]* and move faster *[1 mark]*. The forces between the particles are weakened *[1 mark]*. At the boiling point, the particles have enough energy to break these forces *[1 mark]*.

b) For each gas, the scientist will see the gas slowly diffusing through the air until both jars are a uniform pale brown colour *[1 mark]*. The mixing of the air and Br_2/NO_2 particles is due to the random motion of the gaseous particles *[1 mark]*. This mixing will occur faster for the NO_2 particles / the NO_2 particles will diffuse into the air faster than the Br_2 particles *[1 mark]*, because NO_2 particles are lighter than Br_2 particles, so they can move more quickly through the air *[1 mark]*.

c) E.g. the bromine gas would diffuse very quickly (from the flask to the chamber) *[1 mark]* because there would be no air particles for the bromine particles to collide with *[1 mark]*.

2 a) A *[1 mark]*

b) i)

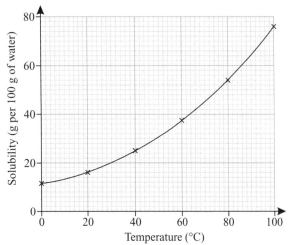

[1 mark for each correct labelled axis, 1 mark for all points correctly plotted, 1 mark for curved line of best fit]

ii) From the graph, 30 °C gives a solubility of 20 g per 100 g of water. So the amount of compound that will dissolve in 25 g of water = (20 ÷ 100) × 25 = 5.0 g.
[2 marks for correct answer according to graph drawn in part i), otherwise 1 mark for reading correct solubility at 30 °C off the graph]

Pages 3-6 — Elements, Compounds and Mixtures

1 a) i) Relative atomic mass (A_r)
= (sum of (isotope abundance × isotope mass number))
÷ sum of abundances of all the isotopes
= ((24 × 79) + (25 × 10) + (26 × 11)) ÷ (79 + 10 + 11)
= 2432 ÷ 100 = 24.32 = **24.3** to 1 d.p. *[1 mark for reading off correct values from y-axis, 1 mark for correct calculation, 1 mark for correct answer to one decimal place]*

ii) magnesium *[1 mark]*

b) i) 12 *[1 mark]*
The number of electrons is equal to the atomic number.

ii) There is an equal number of positively-charged protons and negatively-charged electrons, so the charges cancel each other out to leave a neutral atom *[1 mark]*.

2 a) E.g.
Technique 1: filtration *[1 mark]*
Explanation: copper sulfate will dissolve in the water, silicon dioxide won't. Filtering separates the silicon dioxide from the solution *[1 mark]*.
Technique 2: crystallisation *[1 mark]*
Explanation: crystals of copper sulfate will form as water evaporates *[1 mark]*.

b) Fractional distillation *[1 mark]*. Fractional distillation allows substances with close boiling points to be separated *[1 mark]* because it provides a temperature gradient/is hot at the bottom and cool at the top *[1 mark]*, so only substances with a specific boiling point can reach the top (and be separated off) without condensing and running back into the flask *[1 mark]*.
You need to specify fractional distillation if you want to get all the marks in this question. However, if you just wrote "distillation" then you can still gain a mark for saying that substances with different boiling points will be separated off at different times.

c) e.g. chromatography *[1 mark]*
Unlike distillation, this doesn't involve heating the mixture, which would lead to unwanted reactions *[1 mark]*.

d) E.g. in crystallisation the water/solvent evaporates into the air and is not collected *[1 mark]*.
If you wanted to collect the water, you could use simple distillation.

3 a) 120 mg = 0.120 g *[1 mark]*
percentage = (0.120 ÷ 5) × 100 = **2.4%** *[1 mark]*

b) The different substances will move up the paper at different rates *[1 mark]*, depending on how easily they dissolve in the solvent (and their affinity for the paper) *[1 mark]*. The substances that dissolve more easily in the solvent (or have a lower affinity for the paper) are carried further up the paper *[1 mark]*.

c) distance moved by propyl paraben = 1.8 cm
distance moved by solvent = 4.2 cm
R_f = 1.8 ÷ 4.2 = **0.43** (2 s.f.) (allow between 0.40 and 0.46)
[3 marks for correct answer to two significant figures, otherwise 1 mark for both distances correctly measured within 0.1 cm and 1 mark for correct equation.]

d) Distance moved = 0.52 × 4.2 = **2.2 cm** (2 s.f.)
Spot drawn at 2.2 cm from baseline.
[3 marks for correct answer, correctly marked on diagram, otherwise 1 mark for correct equation to calculate distance and 1 mark for 2.2 cm]

e) The contaminant is not pure *[1 mark]*. It melts over a range of temperatures and pure substances melt at specific temperatures *[1 mark]*.

4 a) The substance may boil over a range of temperatures *[1 mark]*.

b) Run **Z** alongside pure samples of **A**, **B**, and **C** *[1 mark]*. If the spot from **A**, **B** or **C** moves the same distance as **Z**, then it indicates that this may be the contaminant / if the R_f value for **A**, **B** or **C** matches that of a component of **Z**, then it indicates that this may be the contaminant *[1 mark]*.

c) E.g. repeat the experiment using different solvents *[1 mark]*. Calculate new R_f values for the substances in each solvent, and see if they still match *[1 mark]*.
Just because the R_f values of two substances match in one solvent doesn't mean they're the same substance. You need to calculate their R_f values in multiple solvents — if they don't match in all of them, they aren't the same.

Section 2 — The Periodic Table and Bonding

Page 7 — The Periodic Table

1 a) i) A *[1 mark]*
   ii) Lithium is on the left-hand side of the periodic table, so it is a metal *[1 mark]*. Metal oxides are basic (so have a pH greater than 7 in solution) *[1 mark]*.
   b) The electronic configuration of aluminium is 2.8.3 *[1 mark]*. Aluminium has three occupied electron shells, so it is in the third period *[1 mark]*. Aluminium has three electrons in its outer shell, so it is in the third group *[1 mark]*.
   c) Caesium chloride *[1 mark]*
   Caesium is more reactive than sodium (because it's closer to the bottom left corner of the periodic table) *[1 mark]* and chlorine is more reactive than iodine (because it's closer to the top right of the periodic table, excluding the noble gases) *[1 mark]*.

Pages 8-11 — Types of Bonding

1 a) E.g.
   Similarities:
   Both have delocalised electrons *[1 mark]*. Both consist of layers of atoms *[1 mark]*.
   Differences:
   Graphite has covalent bonds, whereas copper has metallic bonds *[1 mark]*. Graphite has weak intermolecular forces between its layers, whereas the electrostatic forces of attraction in copper are very strong *[1 mark]*.
   b) In graphite, each carbon atom only forms three covalent bonds with other carbon atoms *[1 mark]*, so has one delocalised electron that is free to move *[1 mark]*.
2 Solid: the light bulb won't light up *[1 mark]*. This is because, in a solid ionic compound, the ions are held in place so can't conduct electricity *[1 mark]*.
   Aqueous: the light bulb will light up *[1 mark]*. This is because, in solution, the ions from the compound separate and are free to move and conduct electricity *[1 mark]*.
3 a)

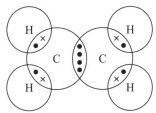

[1 mark for elements correctly labelled, 1 mark for four electrons shared between the two carbon atoms, 1 mark for two electrons shared in each carbon-hydrogen overlap]
   b) Carbon has four electrons in its outer shell *[1 mark]*. Each of these electrons can form part of a shared pair, which forms a covalent bond *[1 mark]*. Three electrons form shared pairs with electrons in hydrogen atoms *[1 mark]*, leaving one electron to form a shared pair with an electron from the other carbon atom *[1 mark]*.
   c) The strong electrostatic attraction between the negatively charged bonding electrons *[1 mark]* and the positively charged nuclei of the carbon and hydrogen atoms *[1 mark]*.
   d) i) A_r of C = 12, A_r of H = 1
   M_r of ethane/C_2H_6 = $(2 \times 12) + (6 \times 1)$ = 30
   M_r of ethene/C_2H_4 = $(2 \times 12) + (4 \times 1)$ = 28
   [1 mark for both correct M_r values]
   ii) To boil a small covalent molecule, the intermolecular forces need to be broken *[1 mark]*. However, the covalent bonds within the molecule are not broken, so their strength does not affect the boiling point *[1 mark]*. Ethane has a higher M_r than ethene so will require more energy to overcome the intermolecular forces / will have a higher boiling point *[1 mark]*.

4 a) Electrons are transferred from magnesium to chlorine *[1 mark]*. The magnesium atoms each lose two electrons to form Mg^{2+} ions *[1 mark]*. The chlorine atoms each gain one electron to form Cl^- ions *[1 mark]*.
There's one Mg^{2+} ion for every two Cl^- ions in the neutral ionic compound $MgCl_2$.
   b) Magnesium oxide contains magnesium ions with a 2+ charge and oxide ions with a 2− charge, whereas sodium chloride contains sodium ions with a 1+ charge and chloride ions with a 1− charge *[1 mark]*. So there are stronger ionic bonds in magnesium oxide than in sodium chloride *[1 mark]*, meaning magnesium oxide has a higher melting point *[1 mark]*.
   c) Cs^+ *[1 mark]*. There is one caesium ion per chloride ion and chloride ions have a 1− charge, so caesium ions must have a 1+ charge (in order to make a neutral ionic compound) *[1 mark]*.
   d) E.g.

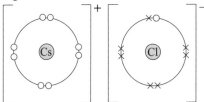

[1 mark for correct charge and electronic structure of caesium ion, 1 mark for correct charge and electronic structure of chloride ion]
   e) $2Cs_{(s)} + Cl_{2(g)} \rightarrow 2CsCl_{(s)}$ *[1 mark for correct formulae, 1 mark for correct balancing]*
5 a) E.g. both are giant covalent structures *[1 mark]*. Diamond contains one type of atom only (carbon), whereas silicon dioxide contains silicon and oxygen *[1 mark]*.
   b) Yes. Both are giant covalent structures with strong covalent bonds *[1 mark]*. Diamond's hardness comes from its rigid lattice structure, and silicon dioxide has a similar structure *[1 mark]*.
   c) Graphite has a layered structure *[1 mark]*. The layers are only held together by weak intermolecular forces *[1 mark]*, so can slide over one another *[1 mark]*.

66

Section 3 — Equations, Calculations and Electrolysis

Pages 12-15 — Moles, Equations and Formulae

1 a) Reaction equation: $CaCO_3 \rightarrow CaO + CO_2$
M_r of CO_2 = 12 + (2 × 16) = 44
Moles of CO_2 = 19.8 ÷ 44 = 0.45 mol
Molar ratio of CO_2 : CaO = 1:1, so moles of CaO = 0.45 mol
M_r of CaO = 40 + 16 = 56
Mass of CaO = 0.45 × 56 = **25.2 g**
[4 marks for the correct answer, otherwise 1 mark for both M_r values, 1 mark for moles of CO_2 and 1 mark for 1:1 molar ratio]

b) Moles of Ca = 30 ÷ 40 = 0.75 mol
Moles of P = 15.5 ÷ 31 = 0.5 mol
Moles of O = 32 ÷ 16 = 2 mol
Dividing 0.75, 0.5 and 2 by 0.5 gives a ratio of 1.5:1:4, which is equivalent to 3:2:8 (Ca:P:O)
Therefore the empirical formula of calcium phosphate(V) is: $Ca_3P_2O_8$
[3 marks for correct empirical formula, otherwise 1 mark for moles of Ca, moles of P and moles of O and 1 mark for 3:2:8 molar ratio]

c) The empirical formula is the simplest formula that tells you the ratio of the different elements in a compound *[1 mark]*, whereas the molecular formula tells you the actual number of atoms of each element in a single molecule of a compound *[1 mark]*.

d) mass of empirical formula = (2 × 31) + (5 × 16) = 142
284 ÷ 142 = 2 empirical units
P_2O_5 × 2 = P_4O_{10} *[3 marks for correct molecular formula, otherwise 1 mark for correct mass of empirical formula and 1 mark for correct number of empirical units]*

2 a) Carbon dioxide is a gas, so it escapes into the air/leaves the container (which reduces the mass) *[1 mark]*.

b) Sodium hydrogencarbonate ($NaHCO_3$) limited the amount of product formed because it was completely used up in an excess of citric acid / before the citric acid *[1 mark]*.

c) Moles of citric acid = mass ÷ M_r = 20.0 ÷ 192 = 0.104... mol
Molar ratio of citric acid : sodium hydrogencarbonate = 1:3 so moles of $NaHCO_3$ = 3 × 0.104... = 0.3125 mol
Mass of $NaHCO_3$ = moles × M_r = 0.3125 × 84
= **26.3 g** (3 s.f.)
[3 marks for the correct answer to 3 significant figures, otherwise 1 mark for moles of citric acid and 1 mark for moles of sodium hydrogencarbonate]

d) M_r of sodium citrate = (6 × 12) + (5 × 1) + (7 × 16) + (3 × 23) = 258
Moles of sodium citrate = mass ÷ M_r = 61.15 ÷ 258 = 0.237... mol
Molar ratio of sodium citrate : citric acid = 1:1, so moles of citric acid = 0.237... mol
mass of citric acid = moles × M_r = 0.237... × 192
= **45.5 g** (3 s.f.)
[3 marks for the correct answer to 3 significant figures, otherwise 1 mark for M_r of sodium citrate and 1 mark for moles of both sodium citrate and citric acid]

3 a) C *[1 mark]*
M_r of sucrose = 342. 6.84 ÷ 342 = 0.02 mol of sucrose, and there are 12 mol of carbon dioxide for every mole of sucrose, so 12 × 0.02 = 0.24 mol of CO_2.

b) Moles of $C_{12}H_{22}O_{11}$ = mass ÷ M_r = 5.13 ÷ 342 = 0.0150 mol
Moles of CO = mass ÷ M_r = 3.36 ÷ 28 = 0.120 mol
Moles of CO_2 = mass ÷ M_r = 2.64 ÷ 44 = 0.0600 mol
Dividing 0.120 and 0.0600 by 0.0150... gives a ratio of 1:8:4 ($C_{12}H_{22}O_{11}$: CO : CO_2)
Therefore equation can be balanced as
$C_{12}H_{22}O_{11}$ + **8**O_2 → **8**CO + **4**CO_2 + **11**H_2O
[3 marks for correctly balanced equation, otherwise 1 mark for moles of CO and moles of CO_2 and 1 mark for a 1:8:4 molar ratio]

c) Moles of sucrose = mass ÷ M_r = 12.0 ÷ 342 = 0.0350... mol
Molar ratio of sucrose : carbon = 1:12, so
0.0350... × 12 = 0.4210... mol of carbon
Mass of carbon = moles × A_r = 0.4210... × 12 = 5.0526...
= **5.05 g** (3 s.f.) *[3 marks for the correct answer to 3 significant figures, otherwise 1 mark for moles of sucrose and 1 mark for moles of carbon]*

4 a) M_r of $CuCO_3$ = 63.5 + 12 + (3 × 16) = 123.5
Moles of $CuCO_3$ = mass ÷ M_r = 12.0 ÷ 123.5 = 0.09716... mol
Molar ratio of $CuCO_3$: CuO = 1:1, so
moles of CuO = moles of $CuCO_3$ = 0.09716... mol
Theoretical yield of CuO = moles × M_r = 0.09716... × 79.5
= 7.724... g
Percentage yield = (actual yield of product ÷ theoretical yield of product) × 100
= (5.10 ÷ 7.724...) × 100 = 66.022... = **66.0%** (3 s.f.)
[5 marks for the correct answer to 3 significant figures, otherwise 1 mark for M_r of $CuCO_3$, 1 mark for moles of both $CuCO_3$ and CuO, 1 mark for theoretical yield of CuO and 1 mark for equation for percentage yield]

b) Mass of H_2O = 34.9 − 22.3 = 12.6 g
Moles of H_2O = 12.6 ÷ 18 = 0.7 mol
Moles of $CuSO_4$ = 22.3 ÷ 159.5 = 0.139... mol
Dividing 0.139... and 0.7 by 0.139 gives a ratio of 1:5.006..., so x = 5.006... = **5**
[1 mark for mass of H_2O, 1 mark for moles of H_2O, 1 mark for moles of $CuSO_4$, 1 mark for correct whole number answer]
'x' has to be a whole number. However, a slight difference from a whole number in experimental results is expected because errors are likely to occur.

Pages 16-17 — Gases and Concentrations

1 a) Moles of sulfuric acid = concentration × volume
= 2 × (22.5 ÷ 1000) = 0.045 mol
Molar ratio of potassium carbonate : sulfuric acid = 1:1, so moles of potassium carbonate = moles of sulfuric acid = 0.045 mol
Concentration of potassium carbonate solution
= moles ÷ volume = 0.045 ÷ (25 ÷ 1000)
= **1.80 mol/dm³** *[2 marks for the correct answer to 3 significant figures, otherwise 1 mark for moles of both sulfuric acid and potassium carbonate]*
If the concentration is given in mol/dm³ then make sure you convert any volumes to dm³.

b) moles of potassium carbonate = concentration × volume
= 2.00 × (25 ÷ 1000) = 0.050 mol
mass = moles × M_r = 0.050 × 138 = **6.9 g**
[2 marks for the correct answer, otherwise 1 mark for moles of potassium carbonate]

c) Moles of potassium carbonate = mass ÷ M_r = 0.552 ÷ 138
= 0.004 mol
Molar ratio of potassium carbonate : carbon dioxide = 1:1, so moles of carbon dioxide = moles of potassium carbonate
= 0.004 mol
Volume of carbon dioxide = moles × 24 = 0.004 × 24
= 0.096 dm³ = **96.0 cm³** *[3 marks for the correct answer in cm³, otherwise 1 mark for moles of both potassium carbonate and carbon dioxide and 1 mark for volume in dm³ or molar volume of 24 000 cm³]*

Answers

d) Concentration of potassium carbonate solution in mol/dm^3
= concentration in g/dm^3 ÷ M_r = 234.6 ÷ 138 = 1.70 mol/dm^3
Moles of potassium carbonate = concentration × volume
= 1.70 × (25 ÷ 1000) = 0.0425 mol
Molar ratio of potassium carbonate : sulfuric acid = 1:1, so
moles of sulfuric acid = 0.0425 mol
Volume of sulfuric acid = moles ÷ concentration
= 0.0425 ÷ 2.00 = 0.02125 dm^3 = **21.3 cm^3** (3 s.f.)
[4 marks for correct answer to 3 significant figures,
otherwise 1 mark for concentration of potassium carbonate
solution in mol/dm^3 or mass of potassium carbonate in
solution, 1 mark for moles of both potassium carbonate and
sulfuric acid and 1 mark for volume of sulfuric acid in dm^3]

Alternatively, you could have divided the concentration in g/dm^3
by the volume of potassium carbonate solution to get the mass of
potassium carbonate in the solution, then divided this by the M_r of
potassium carbonate to get the number of moles of potassium carbonate.

2 a) Moles of oxygen gas = volume ÷ 24 = (60 ÷ 1000) ÷ 24
= 0.0025 mol *[1 mark]*

b) Moles of hydrogen peroxide in 1 dm^3 = mass ÷ M_r = 60 ÷ 34
= 1.7647... mol
Moles in 100 cm^3 (0.1 dm^3) = 1.7647... × (100 ÷ 1000)
= 0.17647... mol
Molar ratio of hydrogen peroxide : oxygen gas = 2:1, so
moles of oxygen gas = 0.17647... ÷ 2 = 0.088235... mol
Volume of oxygen gas = moles × 24 = 0.088235... × 24
= **2.1 dm^3** (2 s.f) *[4 marks for the correct answer to 2*
significant figures, otherwise 1 mark for moles of hydrogen
peroxide in 1 dm^3, 1 mark for moles of hydrogen peroxide
in 100 cm^3, and 1 mark for moles of oxygen gas]

Pages 18-19 — Electrolysis

1 B *[1 mark]*

2 a) Cations/positive ions in the electrolyte move towards the
cathode/negative electrode *[1 mark]* and anions/negative ions
move toward the anode/positive electrode *[1 mark]*.

b) Sodium ions are reduced/gain electrons at the negative
electrode/cathode to produce sodium *[1 mark]*.
$Na^+ + e^- \rightarrow Na$ *[1 mark]*
Bromide ions are oxidised/lose electrons at the positive
electrode/anode to produce bromine *[1 mark]*.
$2Br^- \rightarrow Br_2 + 2e^-$ *[1 mark]*

c) In the electrolysis of an aqueous solution, water molecules
will be ionised/there will be H$^+$ and OH$^-$ ions present
[1 mark]. Sodium is more reactive than hydrogen *[1 mark]*
so H$_2$ will be discharged at the cathode/the sodium ions will
remain in the solution/sodium will not be extracted *[1 mark]*.
In molten sodium bromide there are no competing H$^+$ ions, so
sodium is extracted/discharged at the cathode *[1 mark]*.

3 a) A *[1 mark]*
Dilute hydrochloric acid, aqueous potassium chloride and aqueous sodium
chloride will all produce chlorine gas at the anode and hydrogen gas at the
cathode. Molten zinc chloride will produce chlorine gas at the anode and
zinc at the cathode This is because it is not in aqueous solution, so there
are no competing hydrogen ions.

b) The electrodes are usually made from an inert material so
that they don't take part in the reactions that occur during
electrolysis *[1 mark]*.

4 a) Potassium hydroxide (KOH) *[1 mark]*
It can't be potassium sulfate (K$_2$SO$_4$) because sulfate ions do not contain
hydrogen. Therefore molten potassium sulfate would not produce water at
the anode.

b) Oxidation: $4OH^- \rightarrow O_2 + 2H_2O + 4e^-$ *[1 mark]*
Reduction: $2H^+ + 2e^- \rightarrow H_2$ *[1 mark]*

c) Potassium is more reactive than hydrogen so potassium/K$^+$
ions remain in solution *[1 mark]* whilst hydrogen/H$^+$ ions are
reduced at the cathode to form hydrogen gas *[1 mark]*.

Section 4 — Inorganic Chemistry

Pages 20-21 — Alkali Metals and Halogens

1 a) Astatine will consist of diatomic covalently bonded
molecules *[1 mark]*. It is a Group 7 element / has 7 electrons
in its outer shell/energy level *[1 mark]* so will form one
covalent bond with another atom of astatine *[1 mark]*.

b) Astatine will be a solid at room temperature *[1 mark]* as the
melting/boiling point of halogens increases as you go down
the group, and iodine is a solid *[1 mark]*.

c) There will be no reaction *[1 mark]*. Astatine is less reactive
than chlorine, so cannot displace chloride from a salt solution
[1 mark].

d) The outer shell/energy level of rubidium atoms is far from
the nucleus, so the electrons are weakly held *[1 mark]*.
Therefore little energy is required to remove the single
electron in rubidium's outer shell/energy level *[1 mark]*.
The outer shell/energy level of iodine atoms is far from the
nucleus *[1 mark]*, so it is hard for them to attract electrons
[1 mark].

2 a) The mass of the sample would increase *[1 mark]* as the
lithium reacts with/takes on oxygen from the air to form
lithium oxide (Li$_2$O) *[1 mark]*

b) $2Li_{(s)} + 2H_2O_{(l)} \rightarrow 2LiOH_{(aq)} + H_{2(g)}$
[1 mark for correct equation, 1 mark for correct balancing,
1 mark for correct state symbols]

c) Similarity:
E.g. both metals float on the surface of the water / both
reactions are vigorous / in both reactions there is fizzing/
bubbles/gas given off / in both reactions the metal disappears
[1 mark].
Explanation:
E.g. both lithium and potassium have one electron in their
outer electron shell/energy level that is easily lost, so they are
both highly reactive *[1 mark]*.
Difference:
E.g. the potassium will move across the surface of the water
more quickly / the reaction with potassium will be more
vigorous / the reaction with potassium will produce more
fizzing/bubbles/gas / potassium will disappear/react faster
/ potassium will melt and ignite, producing a lilac flame
[1 mark].
Explanation:
E.g. the outer shell/energy level of potassium atoms is further
from the nucleus than in lithium, so the outer electron is
more easily lost (making potassium more reactive) *[1 mark]*.

3 a) The solution would turn brown/become darker *[1 mark]* as
chlorine displaces iodine from solution *[1 mark]*, because
chlorine is more reactive than iodine *[1 mark]*.

b) i) In a redox reaction, reduction and oxidation happen at the
same time / electrons are lost by one reactant and gained by
another *[1 mark]*.

ii) The chlorine is reduced/gains electrons to form chloride ions
[1 mark]. The iodide ions are oxidised/lose electrons to form
iodine *[1 mark]*.

c) If you added chlorine water to sodium bromide, the solution
would go from colourless to orange *[1 mark]*. This is
because chlorine is more reactive than bromine, so would
displace bromine from the solution *[1 mark]*. If you added
chlorine water to sodium chloride, there would be no reaction
/ no colour change would be seen *[1 mark]*. This is because
the solution already contains chloride ions / chlorine cannot
displace itself from solution *[1 mark]*.

Pages 22-23 — Gases and Their Reactions

1 a) Nitrogen: 78% (allow 78-80%)
Oxygen: 21% (allow 20-21%)
Argon: nearly 1% (allow 0.9-1.0%)
[2 marks for all three answers correct, otherwise 1 mark for two answers correct]

b) Venus' atmosphere has a much higher percentage of CO_2 than Earth's atmosphere *[1 mark]*. CO_2 is a greenhouse gas *[1 mark]*. Greenhouse gases absorb most of the heat that would normally be radiated out to space and re-radiate it in all directions, including back towards the planet *[1 mark]*. This warms/insulates the planet (which contributes to a higher average surface temperature) *[1 mark]*.

2 $Mg + 0.5O_2 \rightarrow MgO$ / $2Mg + O_2 \rightarrow 2MgO$ *[1 mark]*
$S + O_2 \rightarrow SO_2$ *[1 mark]*
E.g. the container in which sulfur was burnt will have the lower percentage of oxygen gas, because the number of moles of oxygen gas required for the complete combustion of the sulfur is larger than the number of moles of oxygen gas required for the complete combustion of the magnesium *[1 mark]*.

3 a) E.g.

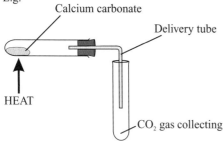

Calcium carbonate
Delivery tube
HEAT
CO_2 gas collecting

[1 mark for calcium carbonate in sealed tube connected to a suitable collection vessel via delivery tube, 1 mark for heat applied to calcium carbonate and 1 mark for carbon dioxide gas collecting in bottom of collection vessel]

You could also collect the gas using a water displacement method or a gas syringe.

b) E.g. connect a gas syringe filled with the air sample to another empty gas syringe via a tube containing phosphorus *[1 mark]*. Heat the phosphorus, using the syringes to pass air over it *[1 mark]*. The phosphorus will react with oxygen in the air, removing it from the air and reducing the volume *[1 mark]*. Measure the reduction in volume and use it to calculate the percentage of oxygen in the air *[1 mark]*.

c) Percentage of oxygen = $((50.0 - 39.5) \div 50.0) \times 100$
= 21.0 % *[1 mark]*

d) E.g. the air sample had the same percentage of oxygen as atmospheric air *[1 mark]*. This suggests that air was exchanged between the inside and outside of the container / oxygen was able to enter the container *[1 mark]*.

If the container had been sealed, then a lower percentage of oxygen gas would be expected. This is because oxygen is used up in the reaction with calcium without being replaced.

Pages 24-27 — Reactivity of Metals

1 a) Titanium does not react with sodium chloride/sodium compounds *[1 mark]*.

b) E.g. iron does not need to be removed from rutile / there is a higher proportion of titanium in rutile *[1 mark]*.

c) Any two from: e.g. titanium chloride needs to be purified / there are many stages / electrolysis requires a lot of energy *[2 marks — 1 mark for each correct answer]*

d) $TiCl_4 + 2Mg \rightarrow 2MgCl_2 + Ti$ *[1 mark for correct formulae of reactants and products, 1 mark for balancing]*

e) Magnesium is more reactive than carbon / above carbon in the reactivity series, so magnesium chloride will not be reduced by heating with carbon *[1 mark]*.

2 a) No reaction would take place *[1 mark]* because copper is below iron in the reactivity series (therefore cannot displace it) *[1 mark]*.

b) Zinc is oxidised *[1 mark]*
$Zn \rightarrow Zn^{2+} + 2e^-$ *[1 mark]*
The zinc is oxidised because it loses electrons — it goes from being Zn to Zn^{2+}.

c) Equation: $Mg_{(s)} + CuSO_{4(aq)} \rightarrow MgSO_{4(aq)} + Cu_{(s)}$ *[1 mark for correct formulae of products, 1 mark for state symbols]*
Explanation: The orange-brown solid is a coating of copper, which is displaced from the solution *[1 mark]*. The colour fades as blue copper sulfate solution reacts to form colourless magnesium sulfate solution *[1 mark]*.

d) There is only a small difference in reactivity/calcium is only a little bit more reactive than magnesium *[1 mark]*.

e) A *[1 mark]*.

3 a) The magnesium blocks are used for sacrificial protection/ to prevent the steel from rusting *[1 mark]*. Magnesium is more reactive than iron so reacts in preference to the steel *[1 mark]*. Metals above magnesium would be too reactive/ react with the water quickly *[1 mark]*, and metals below iron (e.g. copper) would not be reactive enough, so the iron would rust *[1 mark]*.

b) E.g. copper *[1 mark]* as it is the least reactive of the metals / lowest in the reactivity series, so will not corrode/react with the water *[1 mark]*. Copper is also a good conductor of heat, so will transfer heat to its surroundings quickly *[1 mark]*.

c) Any three from: e.g. relatively high densities / high melting points / high tensile strength / malleable / lustrous (shiny) / good conductors of electricity/heat.
[3 marks — 1 mark for each correct answer]

d) E.g. aluminium forms a protective oxide layer on its surface, which makes it resistant to corrosion *[1 mark]*. It is also lightweight/less dense than iron or copper, so the cans are portable/easy to transport *[1 mark]*.

4 a) i) e.g. $100 - (4.5 + 0.6 + 1.5 + 0.5) = 92.9\%$ aluminium
$(92.9 \div 100) \times 68\,500 = 63\,636.5$
= **63 600 kg** (to 3 s.f.)
[2 marks for the correct answer, otherwise 1 mark for correct working]

ii) E.g. magnesium is above aluminium in the reactivity series/more reactive than aluminium *[1 mark]*, so an alloy containing a higher percentage of magnesium would be less resistant to corrosion *[1 mark]*.

b) The different elements in stainless steels have different sized atoms *[1 mark]*. This distorts the layers of iron atoms *[1 mark]*, making it more difficult for them to slide over each other *[1 mark]*.

c) E.g. low carbon steel is malleable, whereas stainless steels are hard / low carbon steel is cheaper than stainless steel *[1 mark]*.

d) E.g. high carbon steel is composed mostly of iron, which corrodes/rusts in contact with oxygen and water *[1 mark]*. The paint coats the steel and serves as a barrier to oxygen and water *[1 mark]*.

Pages 28-31 — Acids and Their Reactions

1 a) 13.0 cm³ *[1 mark]*
This is the volume of HCl added when the pH = 7.

b) Reaction equation: $NaOH + HCl \rightarrow NaCl + H_2O$
Moles of hydrochloric acid = concentration × volume
= $0.035 \times 0.25 = 0.00875$ mol
Molar ratio of sodium hydroxide : hydrochloric acid = 1:1, so moles of sodium hydroxide = moles of hydrochloric acid
= 0.00875 mol
Mass of sodium hydroxide = moles × M_r = 0.00875×40
= 0.35 g *[3 marks for the correct answer, otherwise 1 mark for 0.00875 moles of hydrochloric acid, 1 mark for a 1:1 molar ratio or 0.00875 moles of sodium hydroxide]*

Answers

c) The hydrochloric acid acts as a proton donor, donating a proton to the sodium hydroxide *[1 mark]*. The sodium hydroxide/hydroxide ion acts as a proton acceptor, accepting the proton from the hydrochloric acid *[1 mark]*.

2 a) i) sodium *[1 mark]*

ii) Place a lighted splint into the gas *[1 mark]*. If the gas is hydrogen then it will burn with a squeaky pop *[1 mark]*.

b) i) $Mg(OH)_2 + 2HNO_3 \rightarrow Mg(NO_3)_2 + 2H_2O$
[1 mark for correct equation, 1 mark for balancing]

ii) There will be bubbles/fizzing in the second flask (but not in the first flask) *[1 mark]*, because carbon dioxide gas is produced *[1 mark]*.

iii) magnesium oxide/MgO *[1 mark]*

c) E.g. **MX** is an alkali *[1 mark]*, because it reacts with the acid to neutralise it (as shown by the rise in pH) *[1 mark]* and it is soluble in water *[1 mark]*. **MX** can't be a metal carbonate, because a gas is not produced when **MX** reacts with acid (as shown by the lack of bubbles) *[1 mark]*.

3 a) A (white) solid precipitate would form in the mixture *[1 mark]* because barium sulfate is an insoluble salt *[1 mark]*.

b) Filter out the barium sulfate precipitate by carefully pouring the solution through filter paper (in a filter funnel) into a conical flask *[1 mark]*. Rinse the contents of the filter paper with deionised water to wash away any of the soluble salts *[1 mark]*. Place the barium sulfate on fresh filter paper and leave to dry in an oven/desiccator *[1 mark]*.

c) Copper(II) nitrate is soluble *[1 mark]*.

d) $Cu(OH)_{2(s)} + 2HNO_{3(aq)} \rightarrow Cu(NO_3)_{2(aq)} + 2H_2O_{(l)}$
[1 mark for correctly identifying water as the other product, 1 mark for correctly balanced equation and 1 mark for correct state symbols]

e) Heat the solution gently with a Bunsen burner to slowly evaporate off some of the water *[1 mark]*. Leave the solution to cool and allow the copper(II) nitrate to crystallise *[1 mark]*. Then filter off the solid salt crystals and leave them to dry *[1 mark]*.

f) i) E.g. add a pH indicator (such as phenolphthalein or methyl orange) to the nitric acid. The indicator will change colour when the acid is completely neutralised (i.e. the reaction is complete) *[1 mark]*.

ii) If the end point is not determined, then the final solution may be contaminated by excess acid/alkali/indicator *[1 mark]*.

4 a) E.g. use a pipette to add 25 cm³ of sulfuric acid to a conical flask, along with a few drops of indicator *[1 mark]*. Fill a burette with the sodium hydroxide solution and slowly add the solution to the conical flask (swirling the flask regularly) *[1 mark]*. Watch for the colour change in the indicator and record the volume of alkali added when the colour changes *[1 mark]*. Repeat the titration a few times to ensure results are reliable *[1 mark]*.

b) C *[1 mark]*
The result of Titration 1 is much lower than that of 2 or 3, so it is anomalous and should be ignored.

c) Moles of sulfuric acid = concentration × volume
= 0.50 × (25 ÷ 1000) = 0.0125 mol
Molar ratio of sodium hydroxide to sulfuric acid is 2:1, so moles of sodium hydroxide = 0.0125 × 2 = 0.0250
Concentration of sodium hydroxide = moles ÷ volume
= 0.0250 ÷ (23.40 ÷ 1000) = 1.06837...
= **1.07 mol dm⁻³** (3 s.f.)
[3 marks for correct answer given to 3 significant figures, otherwise 1 mark for moles of sulfuric acid, 1 mark for moles of sodium hydroxide]

Pages 32-33 — Chemical Tests

1 a) Conduct flame tests using the Bunsen burner and the loop of platinum, cleaning the loop in acid between each test *[1 mark]*. The solution containing lithium will give a red flame and the solution containing potassium will give a lilac flame *[1 mark]*. Add dilute acid to the solutions to determine the presence of carbonate ions *[1 mark]*.
The solution containing carbonate ions will fizz *[1 mark]*. Add dilute nitric acid and silver nitrate to fresh samples of the solutions to determine the presence of halide/chloride ions *[1 mark]*. The solution containing chloride ions will produce a white precipitate *[1 mark]*.

If the tests are carried out in this order then it's important that fresh samples are used to identify the halide ions. This is because both solutions will contain chloride ions after the addition of hydrochloric acid.

b) FeSO₄ *[1 mark]*

2 **A** Sodium iodide (NaI) *[1 mark]*
B Orange-red flame *[1 mark]*
C No visible change *[1 mark]*
D White precipitate *[1 mark]*

3 a) A blue precipitate would form in the solution *[1 mark]*.

b) Ammonia *[1 mark]*. Damp red litmus paper will turn blue in its presence *[1 mark]*.

c) (NH₄)₂CO₃ *[1 mark]*
Ammonia is produced when sodium hydroxide is added to solutions containing NH₄⁺/ammonium ions (so the cation is NH₄⁺) *[1 mark]*. Carbon dioxide turns limewater cloudy *[1 mark]*. It is given off when dilute hydrochloric acid is added to solutions containing CO₃²⁻/carbonate ions (so the anion is CO₃²⁻) *[1 mark]*.

d) Heat the copper(II) sulfate crystals to drive off any water they contain *[1 mark]* and produce white anhydrous copper(II) sulfate crystals *[1 mark]*. Add a couple of drops of the unknown solution to the crystals and if they turn blue, the solution contains water *[1 mark]*.

e) E.g. the unknown solution contains ammonium and carbonate ions, so is impure *[1 mark]*. Therefore the boiling point of the solution will differ from that of pure water/100 °C *[1 mark]*.

Section 5 — Physical Chemistry

Pages 34-36 — Energy Transfer

1 a)

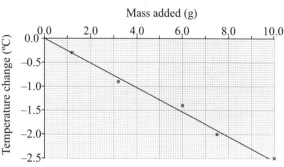

[3 marks — 1 mark for a sensible scale on the axes, 1 mark for all points plotted correctly, 1 mark for a sensible line of best fit that passes through the origin]
Your line of best fit must go through the origin because if no citric acid was added then there would be no temperature change.

b) Answer in the range –1.4 to –1.2 °C
[1 mark for an answer correctly read from the line of best fit drawn in part a)]

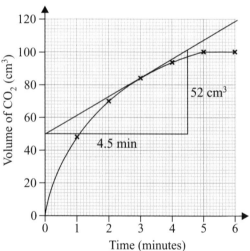

[1 mark for appropriate horizontal or vertical line drawn]

c) E.g. the student kept all variables other than the mass of the citric acid the same *[1 mark]*, which makes the experiment a fair test *[1 mark]*. The student also repeated the experiment for each mass and calculated mean values *[1 mark]*, which improves the reliability of the results *[1 mark]*.

d) E.g. bond breaking is an endothermic process/takes in energy and bond forming is an exothermic process/gives out energy *[1 mark]*. In an endothermic reaction, the energy released by bond formation must be less than the energy absorbed by bond breaking / the total bond energy of the products is less than the total bond energy of the reactants *[1 mark]*.

2 a) Energy released by bonds forming in the products
= 2 × (3 × N–H) = 2 × (3 × 391) = 6 × 391 = 2346 kJ/mol
Overall energy change = energy required to break bonds – energy released by forming bonds, so
Energy required to break bonds = overall energy change + energy released by forming bonds
= –97 + 2346 = 2249 kJ/mol
Energy required to break bonds = (1 × N≡N) + (3 × H–H)
= 941 + (3 × H–H) = 2249 kJ/mol, so
(3 × H–H) = 2249 – 941 = 1308 kJ/mol
H–H bond energy = 1308 ÷ 3 = **436 kJ/mol**
[4 marks for correct answer, otherwise 1 mark for correct energy released by forming bonds, 1 mark for correct energy required to break bonds and 1 mark for (3 × H–H)]

b) The overall energy change is negative *[1 mark]*, so more energy is released in making bonds than is absorbed in breaking bonds *[1 mark]*.

3 a) The energy of the reactants is higher than the energy of the products *[1 mark]*, so energy has been released during the reaction *[1 mark]*.

b) Heat energy transferred (Q) = m × c × ΔT
= 25 × 4.2 × 8.9 = 934.5 J
Heat energy transferred per gram = 934.5 ÷ 0.3 g
= 3115 J ≈ **3.1 kJ** (2 s.f.) *[3 marks for correct answer to two significant figures, otherwise 1 mark for correct equation for heat energy transferred and 1 mark for calculation of heat energy transferred per gram]*

c) M_r of butanol = (4 × 12) + (10 × 1) + (1 × 16) = 74 g/mol
Moles of butanol = 2.22 ÷ 74 = 0.03 mol
Molar enthalpy change = –80.1 ÷ 0.03
= **–2670 kJ/mol** *[4 marks for correct answer, otherwise 1 mark for M_r of butanol, 1 mark for moles of butanol and 1 mark for calculation of molar enthalpy change]*

Pages 37-40 — Rates of Reaction

1 a) B *[1 mark]*
The size of the measuring cylinder won't affect the results so long as the correct volume is still measured out.

b) E.g. with 20 cm³ of $Na_2S_2O_3$ solution the time taken is 22 s and with 10 cm³ the time taken is 44 s, so doubling the volume halves the time/doubles the rate of reaction *[1 mark]*. Doubling the volume doubles the concentration / the volume is proportional to the concentration *[1 mark]*.
In this experiment, the volume of $Na_2S_2O_3$ solution is proportional to its concentration because the total volume of $Na_2S_2O_3$ solution and water is kept the same. So if more $Na_2S_2O_3$ solution is used, less water must be used and the concentration will be higher.

c) Doubling the concentration doubles the number of particles in the same volume *[1 mark]*. This doubles the frequency of (successful) collisions *[1 mark]*.

d) Increasing the temperature makes the particles move faster *[1 mark]* so the particles collide more frequently and the rate increases *[1 mark]*. The particles also collide with more energy *[1 mark]* so more of the collisions are successful / have sufficient energy to react / have the activation energy *[1 mark]*.

2 a)

Gradient = change in y ÷ change in x
= (102 – 50) ÷ (4.5 – 0) = 11.555... = **12 cm³/min**
[3 marks for answer between 11 cm³/min and 13 cm³/min given to two significant figures, otherwise 1 mark for correctly drawn tangent to curve at 3 minutes and 1 mark for correct equation for the gradient]

b) The gradient of the graph is initially steep, but it starts to decrease / get less steep as time increases *[1 mark]*, so less carbon dioxide is produced in a given amount of time *[1 mark]*.

c) A *[1 mark]*

3 a)

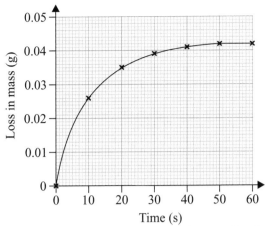

[1 mark for correct calculation of loss in mass (y) values, 2 marks for all points plotted correctly, or 1 mark for at least 5 points plotted correctly, 1 mark for sensible scale used on axes, 1 mark for line of best fit.]

b)

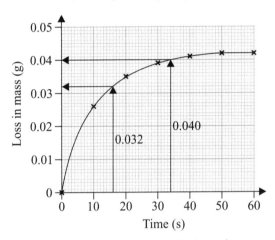

Mean rate of reaction = change in y ÷ change in x
= (0.040 − 0.032) ÷ (34 − 16) = 0.008 ÷ 18 = 0.000444...
= **0.00044 g/s** (2 s.f.) *[3 marks for answer between 0.00039 and 0.0005, otherwise 1 mark for a change in loss in mass between 0.007 and 0.009 and 1 mark for equation to calculate mean rate of reaction]*

4 a) The greater the mass of catalyst, the greater the volume of gas collected in 60 seconds *[1 mark]*. A greater mass of powdered catalyst provides more surface area for collisions/the reaction to take place on *[1 mark]*.

b)

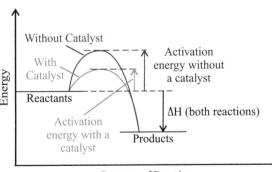

[1 mark for start and end energies being the same for reaction with and without catalyst, 1 mark for label indicating no difference in enthalpy change, 1 mark for reactants with higher energy than products, 1 mark for higher activation energy without catalyst]

c) E.g. filter off the catalyst after the reaction, then wash and dry it *[1 mark]*. Reweigh the catalyst and compare the masses before and after the reaction *[1 mark]*. The catalyst is not used up during the reaction, therefore there should be no change in mass *[1 mark]*.

Pages 41-42 — Reversible Reactions

1 a) As the reaction progresses, the amount of iodine monochloride and chlorine gas decreases, so the forward reaction slows down *[1 mark]*, but as more iodine trichloride is made, the backwards reaction speeds up *[1 mark]*. After a while, the forward and backward reactions will be going at the same rate/the reaction will reach equilibrium *[1 mark]*. The quantities of reactants and products will have reached a balance and will not change *[1 mark]*.
Remember that in a closed system nothing can leave or enter — this is what allows the system to reach equilibrium.

b) Time = 80 seconds *[1 mark]*
This is the time when both lines become horizontal and therefore the concentrations of products and reactants do not change.

c) i) B *[1 mark]*
   ii) The position of equilibrium would move to the left because there are more gaseous molecules on the left *[1 mark]*, so more iodine monochloride (the dark brown liquid) would be formed and less iodine trichloride (the yellow solid) would be present *[1 mark]*.

d) More iodine trichloride has formed *[1 mark]*. Lowering the temperature has moved the equilibrium to the right/towards the products *[1 mark]*, so the forward reaction is exothermic *[1 mark]*.

e) The addition of a catalyst would have no effect on the yield of iodine monochloride *[1 mark]*. A catalyst would increase the rate of the forward and backward reactions by the same amount *[1 mark]*, so the position of equilibrium would not move *[1 mark]*.

2 Temperature: the percentage yield of SO_3 increases as the temperature decreases/the forward reaction is exothermic *[1 mark]*, therefore lowering the temperature will cause the equilibrium to shift to the right and increase the percentage yield *[1 mark]*.
Pressure: there are more moles of gas on the left-hand side of the equation than on the right-hand side *[1 mark]*, therefore a higher pressure will cause the equilibrium to shift to the right and provide a higher percentage yield *[1 mark]*.

Section 6 — Organic Chemistry

Pages 43-45 — Organic Compounds and Crude Oil

1 a) Hydrocarbon A = $C_{10}H_{22}$ *[1 mark]*
Hydrocarbon B = C_8H_{18} *[1 mark]*
Hydrocarbon C = C_2H_4 *[1 mark]*

b) An explanation is given that links some of these points:
Hydrocarbon A is a shorter chain hydrocarbon than $C_{35}H_{72}$.
Hydrocarbon A will be less viscous than $C_{35}H_{72}$.
Hydrocarbon A will be more volatile/have a lower boiling point than $C_{35}H_{72}$.
Hydrocarbon A will be more flammable/easier to ignite than $C_{35}H_{72}$.
Hydrocarbon A is more useful as a fuel than $C_{35}H_{72}$.
Hydrocarbon A/decane is used in fuels such as kerosene.
[1 mark for each point referenced in answer, up to 6 marks]

c) $C_{12}H_{26} \rightarrow 3C_2H_4 + C_6H_{14}$ *[1 mark]*

2 a) C_8H_{18} *[1 mark]*

b) $C_8H_{18} + 12.5O_2 \rightarrow 8CO_2 + 9H_2O$ or,
$2C_8H_{18} + 25O_2 \rightarrow 16CO_2 + 18H_2O$
[1 mark for correct products, 1 mark for correct balancing]

c) E.g. $C_8H_{18} + 9O_2 \rightarrow 2C + 3CO + 3CO_2 + 9H_2O$
[1 mark for correct products, 1 mark for correct balancing]
You must include C and CO_2, but CO and CO_2 don't need to be there (or you can just have one of them).

d) Carbon monoxide *[1 mark]*. It combines with red blood cells / stops red blood cells carrying oxygen around the body *[1 mark]*. High levels of carbon monoxide can lead to fainting, a coma or death *[1 mark]*.

e) Burning hydrocarbons generates lots of heat *[1 mark]*, which allows the nitrogen and oxygen in the air inside car engines to react *[1 mark]*.

f) Nitrogen oxides and sulfur dioxide mix with water vapour in clouds *[1 mark]* to form dilute acids (nitric and sulfuric acid) which fall as rain *[1 mark]*. The acid rain increases acidity/lowers pH in lakes, which can kill plants and animals *[1 mark]*.

3 a) C *[1 mark]*
There is a carbon atom with 5 bonds.

b) Propene *[1 mark]*

c)

[1 mark]
E.g. the structure has the same (molecular) formula/it is C_4H_8/it has the same number of carbon and hydrogen atoms as the structure drawn by the student, and it contains a double bond / The structure is another isomer of butene. / The structure is but-2-ene rather than but-1-ene. *[1 mark]*

d) E.g. the student's statement is incorrect. The double carbon bond can open up so that the carbon atoms can bond with other atoms (therefore butene is unsaturated) *[1 mark]*.

Pages 46-49 — Reactions of Organic Compounds

1 a) Step 1: react propene with steam in the presence of a catalyst, to form propanol *[1 mark]*.
Step 2: react propanol with an oxidising agent/oxygen to form propanoic acid *[1 mark]*.

b)

[1 mark]

c) The carbon-carbon/C=C double bond breaks and a bromine atom is added to each of the carbon atoms *[1 mark]*.
Bromine is now part of a new molecule/compound/the product which is colourless *[1 mark]*.

d) i) $C_3H_8 + Cl_2 \rightarrow C_3H_7Cl + HCl$ *[1 mark for correct reactants, 1 mark for correct products]*

ii) Ultraviolet light *[1 mark]*

e) A hydrogen atom is replaced/substituted for a chlorine/halogen atom *[1 mark]*.

2 a) Glycolic acid has the functional groups of both an alcohol and a carboxylic acid *[1 mark]*.

b) Fizzing is observed *[1 mark]*. The carboxylic acid functional group reacts with sodium carbonate to produce carbon dioxide *[1 mark]*.
$2CH_2OHCOOH_{(s)} + Na_2CO_{3(aq)}$
$\rightarrow 2CH_2OHCOONa_{(aq)} + H_2O_{(l)} + CO_{2(g)}$
[1 mark for correctly balanced equation and 1 mark for correct state symbols]

c) E.g. the alcohol functional group reacts to form a carboxylic acid functional group *[1 mark]*.

d) React glycolic acid with a carboxylic acid/alcohol *[1 mark]* and use an acid catalyst *[1 mark]*.
Either a carboxylic acid or an alcohol can be used because glycolic acid contains both a carboxylic acid and an alcohol functional group.

e)

[1 mark]

3 a)

[1 mark]
butanol/butan-1-ol *[1 mark]*

b) Using an oxidising agent (e.g. potassium dichromate(VI) in dilute sulfuric acid) *[1 mark]*
Using microorganisms/microbial oxidation *[1 mark]*

c) $CH_3CH_2CH_2COOH$ *[1 mark]*

d) i) $C_4H_9OH + 6O_2 \rightarrow 4CO_2 + 5H_2O$ *[1 mark for correct reactants and products, 1 mark for balancing]*

ii) E.g. the reaction is exothermic/it is a combustion reaction during which energy is released as heat *[1 mark]*.

e) E.g. yeast cells added to the glucose produce enzymes *[1 mark]* that convert the glucose into ethanol and carbon dioxide *[1 mark]*. This process is known as fermentation *[1 mark]*. The fermentation mixture needs to be about 30 °C (to increase the rate of reaction without denaturing the yeast) *[1 mark]* and in anaerobic conditions/without air (to prevent the ethanol being converted into ethanoic acid) *[1 mark]*.

4 a)

[1 mark]

b) Esters are volatile/evaporate easily *[1 mark]*, so they easily release molecules that people can smell/taste *[1 mark]*. They have distinctive/sweet smells *[1 mark]*, so can be used to add pleasant scents/flavours to food *[1 mark]*.

c) Alcohol: propanol *[1 mark]*
Carboxylic acid: ethanoic acid *[1 mark]*

d) $CH_3COOH + CH_3CH_2CH_2OH$
$\rightarrow CH_3COOCH_2CH_2CH_3 + H_2O$
[1 mark for the structural formula of ethanoic acid, 1 mark for the structural formula of propanol and 1 mark for water as the other product]

e) E.g. place a few drops of concentrated sulfuric acid in a boiling tube and add drops of the carboxylic acid/ethanoic acid, and an equal volume of alcohol/propanol *[1 mark]*. Place the boiling tube in a beaker of water and heat using a Bunsen burner (for 1 minute) *[1 mark]*. Remove the tube from the water and allow to cool *[1 mark]*. When the mixture is cool, pour it into a test tube of sodium carbonate and mix *[1 mark]*. The ester will form as a layer on top of the mixture *[1 mark]*.

Pages 50-51 — Polymers

1 a) Chlorotrifluoroethane is saturated/has a single C-C bond *[1 mark]*, so chlorotrifluoroethane molecules cannot form bonds between each other to create a single polymer chain *[1 mark]*.

b)

[1 mark for the correct structure of the repeating unit, which shows two carbon atoms with a single bond between them and 1 mark for correctly placed n on each side of the equation]

c) Condensation polymerisation *[1 mark]*
The monomers react together and ester links form between them to make a polymer chain *[1 mark]*. A small molecule/water is lost for every ester link that forms *[1 mark]*.

d)

[1 mark for repeating unit containing both monomers, 1 mark for ester link between monomers and 1 mark for correctly placed brackets and n]

2 a) E.g. addition polymers are inert, so do not react easily *[1 mark]*. This is because of the strong carbon-carbon bonds in the polymer chain, which are not easily broken *[1 mark]*. This means addition polymers take a very long time to break down and stay in landfill sites/the environment for many years *[1 mark]*. The polymers can be burnt, but doing so releases toxic gases into the environment *[1 mark]*.

b) E.g. biopolyesters are polyesters/polymers that are biodegradable/broken down easily by bacteria and other living organisms *[1 mark]*. Because of this, they decompose and don't stay in landfill *[1 mark]*, reducing their environmental impact/pollutant effect *[1 mark]*.

3 a) C *[1 mark]*
Both the alcohol (diol) and carboxylic acid (dicarboxylic acid) must have two functional groups. The part of the repeating unit from the diol has 4 carbon atoms and the part from the dicarboxylic acid has 3 carbon atoms.

b) 1:2 *[1 mark]*

Mixed Questions for Paper 1

Pages 52-57 — Mixed Questions for Paper 1

1 a) A = bromine *[1 mark]*
A more reactive halogen displaces a less reactive halogen from an aqueous solution of its salt *[1 mark]*. A reacts with potassium iodide solution to displace iodine, so A must be a halogen that is more reactive than iodine *[1 mark]*. Chlorine reacts with an aqueous solution of A's salt, so A must be less reactive than chlorine *[1 mark]*.

The only halogen that is more reactive than iodine but less reactive than chlorine is bromine. Remember, the reactivity of the halogens decreases down the group.

b) Z = potassium *[1 mark]*
Formation of a white, soluble (ionic) solid with bromine/vigorous reaction with water to form an alkali implies Z is a Group 1 metal *[1 mark]*.
E.g. the percentage of Z by mass in a metal hydroxide, ZOH $= A_r(Z) \div (A_r(Z) + 16 + 1) \times 100 = 69.64\%$ *[1 mark]*
In order for the percentage mass of Z to equal 69.64%, Z must have an A_r of 39 *[1 mark]* (so Z is potassium).

The percentage mass of Z is Z's A_r divided by the M_r of ZOH. The only way this can be 69.64% is if Z is potassium. Sodium would be 57.50%, lithium would be 29.17%

c) i) KBr *[1 mark]*
ii) E.g. melt X / dissolve X in solution *[1 mark]*.

2 a) i) The level of carbon dioxide has increased between 1960 and 2010 *[1 mark]*. The rate of increase has also risen over time *[1 mark]*.
ii) E.g. the increased amount of carbon dioxide may cause the global mean sea level to rise *[1 mark]*, because carbon dioxide is a greenhouse gas *[1 mark]*, so it acts as an insulating layer in the atmosphere / traps heat radiation / absorbs and re-radiates heat back towards the Earth *[1 mark]*. This increases the average temperature of the Earth, which may cause the polar ice caps to melt *[1 mark]* (which would increase the global mean sea level).

b) Carbon dioxide has a simple molecular structure *[1 mark]*, with weak intermolecular forces between molecules *[1 mark]*. These are easily overcome, giving it a low boiling point *[1 mark]*. Magnesium oxide has a giant ionic lattice structure *[1 mark]*, so has strong electrostatic forces of attraction between ions *[1 mark]*. These require a lot of energy to break, giving it a high melting/boiling point *[1 mark]*.

c) i) thermal decomposition *[1 mark]*
ii) Bubble the gas through limewater *[1 mark]*. If the limewater turns cloudy then the gas is carbon dioxide *[1 mark]*.

3 a) i) $Cl_{2(g)} + 2FeCl_{2(aq)} \rightarrow 2FeCl_{3(aq)}$
[1 mark for balanced equation, 1 mark for state symbols.]
ii) E.g. In order to form $NaCl_2$, sodium would have to form an Na^{2+} ion to balance the charges on the two Cl^- ions *[1 mark]*. Sodium can only form Na^+ ions, so this is not possible *[1 mark]*.

Sodium is in Group 1, so loses one electron to form an Na^+ ion.

b) A purple vapour will form in the beaker *[1 mark]* as the iodine vaporises as it is heated *[1 mark]*. Purple/grey crystals will form on the lid *[1 mark]* as iodine crystallises/solidifies/deposits on the cooled lid *[1 mark]*.

74

c) i) Bromine exists as a simple covalent molecule *[1 mark]* in which two bromine atoms are covalently bonded/share two electrons *[1 mark]*. When bromine reacts with a Group 1 element, an ionic compound is formed *[1 mark]*. This is because the Group 1 atoms easily donate their outer electrons to become positively charged/1+ ions, and the bromine atoms easily accept the electrons to become negatively charged bromide/Br^- ions *[1 mark]*.

ii) moles of bromine = mass ÷ M_r = 20.00 ÷ 160 = 0.125 moles
reaction equation = $Br_2 + 2G \rightarrow 2GBr$
ratio of moles of Br_2 to moles of GBr = 1 : 2
moles of GBr = 0.125 × 2 = 0.250 moles
M_r(GBr) = mass ÷ moles = 25.75 ÷ 0.250 = 103
A_r(G) = M_r(GBr) − A_r(Br) = 103 − 80 = 23
So, G = sodium/Na
[5 marks for correct answer, otherwise 1 mark for correct number of moles of bromine, 1 mark for correct ratio of moles of Br_2 to moles of GBr, 1 mark for correct number of moles of GBr, 1 mark for correct M_r of GBr.]

4 a) calcium carbonate + hydrochloric acid → calcium chloride + carbon dioxide + water *[1 mark]*

b) calcium carbonate/$CaCO_3$/the carbonate ion *[1 mark]*
In acid-base reactions, the acid is the proton donor and the base is the proton acceptor.

c) More gas will be produced in the 60 seconds *[1 mark]*. This is because the surface area/surface area to volume ratio has increased *[1 mark]*, so the acid particles will have a greater area to work on, increasing the frequency of collisions and therefore the rate of reaction *[1 mark]*.

d) Filter the reaction solution using filter paper and a funnel *[1 mark]*, so that the insoluble calcium carbonate is separated from the solution *[1 mark]*. Gently heat the solution to remove some of the water *[1 mark]*. Crystallise the salt solution *[1 mark]*, so that the soluble salt/calcium chloride is separated from the water *[1 mark]*. Filter off the solid salt/calcium chloride and leave to dry *[1 mark]*.
The key to answering this question is knowing that calcium carbonate is insoluble, whereas calcium chloride is soluble.

e) Calcium hydroxide is slightly soluble in water *[1 mark]*, so it could not have been fully separated from the solution by filtration *[1 mark]*.

5 Any value from −185 °C to −109 °C *[1 mark]*
Down Group 0 the size of the atoms/number of electrons/relative atomic mass increases *[1 mark]* so the strength of the intermolecular forces increases *[1 mark]* and therefore more energy is required to separate the atoms *[1 mark]*. Krypton is between argon and xenon in size, so has a higher boiling point than argon, but a lower boiling point than xenon *[1 mark]*.

6 a) E.g. catalytic cracking *[1 mark]*. The long-chain hydrocarbons are vaporised and passed over a silica/alumina catalyst *[1 mark]* at 600 – 700 °C *[1 mark]*. The hydrocarbons then break down to produce a mixture of short-chain alkanes (such as pentane) and alkenes *[1 mark]*.
There are other methods of cracking, but catalytic cracking is the only one you're expected to know the details of for this course.

b) $M_r(C_5H_{12})$ = (12 × 5) + (1 × 12) = 72
moles of C_5H_{12} = mass ÷ M_r = 0.50 ÷ 72 = 0.006944...
Q = molar enthalpy change × moles = 3495 × 0.006944...
= 24.2708... kJ = 24270.8... J
ΔT = Q ÷ (m × c) = 24270.8... ÷ (200 × 4.2)
= 28.8938...
initial temperature = final temperature − ΔT
= 50.4 − 28.8938... = 21.5061...
= **21.5 °C** (3 s.f.)
[5 marks for correct answer, otherwise 1 mark for calculating the M_r of C_5H_{12}, 1 mark for correct moles of C_5H_{12}, 1 mark for correct Q, 1 mark for correct ΔT]

7 a) The iron nail has reacted with oxygen and water/rusted/corroded *[1 mark]*. It has taken on oxygen and water (to form hydrated iron oxide), so it has increased in mass *[1 mark]*.

b) The zinc coating protects the iron in the nail from corrosion/rusting *[1 mark]*. The zinc also provides sacrificial protection for the iron *[1 mark]* because zinc is more reactive than iron *[1 mark]* so water and oxygen will react with/corrode/oxidise the zinc instead of the iron *[1 mark]*.

c) Addition of aqueous sodium hydroxide *[1 mark]* will cause a green precipitate to form if iron(II) ions are present *[1 mark]*. The compound is iron(II) hydroxide/$Fe(OH)_2$ *[1 mark]*.

d) i) reduction/redox *[1 mark]*
The iron oxide loses oxygen to form iron metal, so it is reduced.

ii) mass of oxygen lost = mass of iron oxide − mass of iron
= 1620 − 1260 = 360 g
moles of oxygen lost = mass ÷ A_r = 360 ÷ 16
= 22.5 moles
moles of iron made = mass ÷ A_r = 1260 ÷ 56
= 22.5 moles
ratio of Fe : O = 1 : 1
empirical formula = FeO
[1 mark for calculating the mass of oxygen lost, 1 mark for calculating the moles of both oxygen and iron, 1 mark for correct empirical formula]

Mixed Questions for Paper 2

Pages 58-63 — Mixed Questions for Paper 2

1 a) i) Oxygen gas/O_2 *[1 mark]*
O_2 is formed from the hydroxide/OH^- ions in the water molecules of the aqueous solution *[1 mark]*.

ii) $4OH^- \rightarrow 2H_2O + O_2 + 4e^-$ / $2H_2O \rightarrow 4H^+ + O_2 + 4e^-$
[1 mark for correct equation, 1 mark for correct balancing]

iii) Put a glowing splint into the gas *[1 mark]*. If the gas is oxygen then it will relight the glowing splint *[1 mark]*.

b) i) Copper is still produced at the negative electrode/cathode *[1 mark]* because copper is less reactive than magnesium (and hydrogen) *[1 mark]*. Chlorine is produced at the positive electrode/anode *[1 mark]* because a halogen is always produced if a halide ion is present in the solution *[1 mark]*.

ii) $Cu^{2+} + 2e^- \rightarrow Cu$ *[1 mark]*

c) E.g. silver chloride is insoluble *[1 mark]*, so it will not separate into ions in solution/it will just sink to the bottom of the container *[1 mark]*.
Electrolysis only works on molten or dissolved ionic compounds.

2 a) 1. $ZnS + 1.5O_2 \rightarrow ZnO + SO_2$ or,
$2ZnS + 3O_2 \rightarrow 2ZnO + 2SO_2$ *[1 mark]*
2. $2ZnO + C \rightarrow 2Zn + CO_2$ *[1 mark]*

b) i) E.g. the sulfur dioxide mixes with water vapour in clouds to form acid rain *[1 mark]*. Acid rain acidifies lakes, which can kill aquatic species *[1 mark]*.

ii) Energy required to break original bonds
= (4 × (S = O)) + (4 × (O − H)) + (O = O)
= (4 × 522) + (4 × 459) + 494
= 4418 kJ/mol
Energy released by forming new bonds
= (4 × (S = O)) + (4 × (O − H)) + (4 × (S − O))
= (4 × 522) + (4 × 459) + (4 × 265)
= 4984 kJ/mol
Overall energy change = 4418 − 4984 = −566 kJ/mol
[3 marks for correct answer, otherwise 1 mark for energy used breaking bonds, 1 mark for energy released when bonds are formed]

Answers

iii)

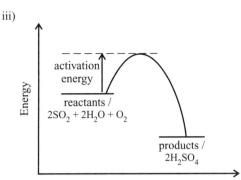

[1 mark for correctly labelled y-axis, 1 mark for correct energy levels of reactants and products, 1 mark for correct shape of curve linking reactants and products and 1 mark for correctly labelled activation energy]

3 a) moles of hydrochloric acid = concentration × volume
= 1.0 × (50 ÷ 1000) = 0.050 mol
Molar ratio of hydrochloric acid : hydrogen gas = 2:1, so
Moles of H_2 = 0.050 ÷ 2 = 0.025 mol
Volume = 24.0 × 0.025 = **0.60 dm^3**
[3 marks for the correct answer, otherwise 1 mark for the correct moles of hydrochloric acid and 1 mark for correct moles of hydrogen gas]

b) Less hydrogen would be produced *[1 mark]*. Calcium has a higher relative atomic mass/A_r than magnesium *[1 mark]* so there will be fewer moles of calcium available to react than there were of magnesium *[1 mark]*.

You could also mention that the calcium would run out before all the acid was used up.

c) Reaction equation:
$Ba(OH)_2 + 2HCl \rightarrow BaCl_2 + 2H_2O$
Ratio of $Ba(OH)_2$: HCl = 1:2,
so moles of $Ba(OH)_2$ required = 0.020 ÷ 2 = 0.010 mol
Volume = moles ÷ concentration = 0.010 ÷ 0.65
= 0.0153... dm^3 = 15.3... cm^3 = **15 cm^3 (2 s.f.)**
[4 marks for correct answer, otherwise 1 mark for reaction equation/correct ratio, 1 mark for correct moles of barium hydroxide, 1 mark for correct volume given in dm^3 or to a different number of significant figures]

d) E.g. theoretical mass of $MgCl_2$ = 12.5 ÷ 60 × 100 = 20.83... g
Moles of $MgCl_2$ = 20.83... ÷ 95 = 0.219... mol
Ratio of $MgCl_2$: $Mg(OH)_2$ = 1:1 (as equation is
$Mg(OH)_2 + 2HCl \rightarrow MgCl_2 + 2H_2O$),
so moles of $Mg(OH)_2$ = 0.219... mol
Mass of $Mg(OH)_2$ = 0.219... × 58 = **12.7 g (3 s.f.)**
[5 marks for correct answer, otherwise 1 mark for calculation to find theoretical mass of $MgCl_2$, 1 mark for theoretical mass of $MgCl_2$, 1 mark for theoretical moles of $MgCl_2$ and 1 mark for moles of $Mg(OH)_2$]

Alternatively, you could have found the actual number of moles of $MgCl_2$ formed (0.1315... mol), then calculated the theoretical moles of $MgCl_2$ (and moles of $Mg(OH)_2$) by dividing by 0.60.

4 a) E.g. calcium/calcium carbonate and propanoic acid *[1 mark]*.

b) E.g. carry out a flame test *[1 mark]* if copper ions are present then a blue-green flame will be seen *[1 mark]*. / Add sodium hydroxide solution to a solution of the compound *[1 mark]* if copper ions are present then a blue precipitate will form *[1 mark]*.

c) i) Copper chloride and potassium carbonate *[1 mark]*
Copper carbonate is an insoluble salt *[1 mark]*, so it can be formed from a precipitation reaction between a soluble copper salt and a soluble carbonate salt *[1 mark]*. Copper chloride and potassium carbonate are both soluble salts *[1 mark]*.

Copper hydroxide and calcium carbonate contain the right ions but are insoluble, so are not suitable.

ii) E.g. make solutions of copper chloride and potassium carbonate by dissolving the powders in deionised water *[1 mark]*.
Combine the solutions in a beaker and stir until all the insoluble copper carbonate has precipitated out *[1 mark]*. Filter the solution using filter paper and a funnel to separate the copper carbonate from the solution *[1 mark]*. Rinse the filter paper with deionised water to make sure all the soluble potassium chloride (which is also produced by the reaction) and any unreacted copper chloride/potassium carbonate have been washed off the solid salt *[1 mark]*. Remove the copper carbonate from the filter paper and leave to dry *[1 mark]*.

5 a) Ammonia has a higher boiling point than the other two gases *[1 mark]*.

b) As the pressure increases, the percentage yield increases *[1 mark]*. The position of the equilibrium shifts to the right-hand side *[1 mark]* because there are fewer moles of gas on the right-hand side of the equation *[1 mark]*.

c) The percentage yield decreases as temperature increases *[1 mark]* because the forward reaction is exothermic *[1 mark]*. Higher temperatures favour the backward (endothermic) reaction/shift the equilibrium to the left *[1 mark]*.

You can tell that the forward reaction is exothermic because the enthalpy change (ΔH) is negative.

d) B *[1 mark]*

6 a) E.g. potassium dichromate(VI) and dilute sulfuric acid *[1 mark]*

Ethanoic acid can also be produced from the microbial oxidation of ethanol.

b)

H—C—C with O double bond, O—C—C—H structure

[1 mark]
Ethyl ethanoate *[1 mark]*

c) The acid is a catalyst *[1 mark]*. It increases the rate of the reaction *[1 mark]* by providing an alternative reaction pathway with a lower activation energy *[1 mark]*.

d) i) $2CH_3COOH + 2K \rightarrow 2CH_3COOK + H_2$
[1 mark for correct equation, 1 mark for correct balancing]

ii) potassium ethanoate *[1 mark]*

iii) Both potassium and sodium react by losing one electron. Sodium's outer electron is closer to the nucleus *[1 mark]*, so it is more strongly attracted to the nucleus *[1 mark]* and therefore is less easily lost *[1 mark]*.

Group 1 metals become more reactive down the group.

The Periodic Table

CE9QI41

Key:

Relative atomic mass	Atomic number →
1	
H	
Hydrogen	
1	

Periods	Group 1	Group 2												Group 3	Group 4	Group 5	Group 6	Group 7	Group 0
1																			4 **He** Helium 2
2	7 **Li** Lithium 3	9 **Be** Beryllium 4												11 **B** Boron 5	12 **C** Carbon 6	14 **N** Nitrogen 7	16 **O** Oxygen 8	19 **F** Fluorine 9	20 **Ne** Neon 10
3	23 **Na** Sodium 11	24 **Mg** Magnesium 12												27 **Al** Aluminium 13	28 **Si** Silicon 14	31 **P** Phosphorus 15	32 **S** Sulfur 16	35.5 **Cl** Chlorine 17	40 **Ar** Argon 18
4	39 **K** Potassium 19	40 **Ca** Calcium 20	45 **Sc** Scandium 21	48 **Ti** Titanium 22	51 **V** Vanadium 23	52 **Cr** Chromium 24	55 **Mn** Manganese 25	56 **Fe** Iron 26	59 **Co** Cobalt 27	59 **Ni** Nickel 28	63.5 **Cu** Copper 29	65 **Zn** Zinc 30		70 **Ga** Gallium 31	73 **Ge** Germanium 32	75 **As** Arsenic 33	79 **Se** Selenium 34	80 **Br** Bromine 35	84 **Kr** Krypton 36
5	85 **Rb** Rubidium 37	88 **Sr** Strontium 38	89 **Y** Yttrium 39	91 **Zr** Zirconium 40	93 **Nb** Niobium 41	96 **Mo** Molybdenum 42	98 **Tc** Technetium 43	101 **Ru** Ruthenium 44	103 **Rh** Rhodium 45	106 **Pd** Palladium 46	108 **Ag** Silver 47	112 **Cd** Cadmium 48		115 **In** Indium 49	119 **Sn** Tin 50	122 **Sb** Antimony 51	128 **Te** Tellurium 52	127 **I** Iodine 53	131 **Xe** Xenon 54
6	133 **Cs** Caesium 55	137 **Ba** Barium 56	139 **La** Lanthanum 57	178 **Hf** Hafnium 72	181 **Ta** Tantalum 73	184 **W** Tungsten 74	186 **Re** Rhenium 75	190 **Os** Osmium 76	192 **Ir** Iridium 77	195 **Pt** Platinum 78	197 **Au** Gold 79	201 **Hg** Mercury 80		204 **Tl** Thallium 81	207 **Pb** Lead 82	209 **Bi** Bismuth 83	209 **Po** Polonium 84	210 **At** Astatine 85	222 **Rn** Radon 86
7	223 **Fr** Francium 87	226 **Ra** Radium 88	227 **Ac** Actinium 89	261 **Rf** Rutherfordium 104	262 **Db** Dubnium 105	266 **Sg** Seaborgium 106	264 **Bh** Bohrium 107	277 **Hs** Hassium 108	268 **Mt** Meitnerium 109	271 **Ds** Darmstadtium 110	272 **Rg** Roentgenium 111								

The Lanthanides (atomic numbers 58-71) and the Actinides (atomic numbers 90-103) are not shown in this table.